APHRODISIACS

APHRODISIACS

HAMLYN

ACKNOWLEDGEMENTS

ILLUSTRATION: Victor Lownes; Lance Dane; Il Collezionista; David May, Edouard Pullirsch;
The British Library; National Gallery of Scotland, Maitland Gift (Title page: Edgar Degas); Curtis
Garratt Limited (additional artwork); Robin Lawrie (alphabet); Galerie F. Welz, private collector
(cover subject: Gustav Klimt). Every effort has been made to trace all copyright holders, but in some
cases this has been impossible. Anyone not acknowledged should write to The Editor, care of the
Publishers.
The botanical plates (numbered 1–14) are by the artist Marilena Pistoia and originally appeared in
Piante della Salute and Frutti della Terra. They are reproduced by permission of the copyright holder
Arnoldo Mondadori Editore.

The editors are also grateful to: M. Billett; A. J. Stevens; Stan Duddy; D. O. Finn; A. Willis;
D. Mailer; V. W. Bethel; Emma Cooper; B. N. Healy; Terry Roeve; A. Hillman; G. A. Ford; Al
Payne; Maurice Estelle; Val Vaux; A. Lund-Revere and J. Gower and of course A. B. M. Letz Puch
– all of whom moved the project forward in different ways.

DESIGN: Grahame Dudley Associates

TYPESETTING: Input Typesetting Ltd, London

ISBN: 0 600 56815 6

Produced by Mandarin Offset
Printed and bound in Hong Kong

INTRODUCTION

The story of aphrodisiacs is quickly told. It needs to be, because the real interest in the subject lies in looking at the information piece by piece, in seeing what other cultures and other times have had to say about sexuality, and comparing it with what we believe. The excitement comes with exploring the never-never land between fact and fantasy.

WHAT ARE APHRODISIACS?

Any substance or activity which stimulates sexual desire and pleasure. They take their name from the Greek goddess of love, but all the world's cultures – ancient and modern, civilized and rural – have their own 'aphrodisiacs'. These range from substances and recipes reputed to inflame passion to erotic practices and techniques which raise human sexuality to an art form. The Arts themselves – literature, painting, music and dance – often have Aphrodite for their Muse. This is an encyclopedia of the foods and potions, arts and literature, practices and techniques which different cultures have dedicated to the goddess of love. We may call them 'erotic', after her son Eros, but without love – the principle she embodies – it is all empty shadow play.

DO APHRODISIACS WORK?

This is a very difficult question. The only possible answer is 'if it works for you it works'. That is not to say that aphrodisiacs can only have, at best, a placebo effect. For all its expertise in marketing, the contemporary pharmaceutical industry, despite its immense investment in research and development, cannot synthesize certain active plant principles (for example codeine). A great many important drugs are derived from the higher plants, but at the same time the pharmacological effect of many traditional herbal remedies has not been fully explored. Nobody really knows what essential oils do in plants or what effect they can have on human beings. Thousands of years of trial and error may have the advantage over Science which must say 'no' when it cannot understand.

Those aphrodisiacs which affect the brain and senses in other ways – erotic images, descriptions or performances – certainly do work. So do the sexual postures which have formed the basis of hundreds of sex manuals – good and bad – down the ages. Variety is the best aphrodisiac and that is what all the concern with sexual posture is really about.

WHY DO WE NEED APHRODISIACS?

The only aphrodisiac which a healthy and affectionate couple need is variety, and that is why this book places such emphasis on techniques and postures. 'Variety and experimentation' are the silent message of even the more impractical and esoteric lovemaking positions. Some may seem alien or absurd to us, but they represent thousands of years and countless thousands of lives of sexual experimentation which is hard to ignore. This book is a list of possibilities – ideas to try and to encourage experimentation. You will not like everything: but then you would not expect to fancy every dish in a comprehensive international menu.

Variety as an aphrodisiac is easily understood. Since the beginning of time couples have needed an interesting and varied sexual diet to avoid boredom in what is essentially a repetitive activity. Strengthening one loving relationship by the simple expedient of using a little imagination is infinitely to be preferred to seeking variety in promiscuous and inevitably shallow relationships.

The bewildering array of foods, drinks, herbs and spices which have been credited with aphrodisiac qualities is a much more difficult area. There is no proof that **any** of them work: the principles employed in making a selection for inclusion in this book will be explained in a moment. First there is the question of why people needed them, or felt they did. Here are a few tentative suggestions:

1. Most of us (at least most of us reading this book) are fortunate enough to have a well-balanced diet. Those who choose to live on cakes or fast food at least know, if only in a general way, that these things do not constitute a healthy diet.

Until relatively recently no such knowledge existed. The rich had the choice of everything, and ate badly by concentrating on meat. The middle class, where one existed, wished only to emulate the rich. The poor had vegetables – often only one vegetable – and insufficient meat. Nobody had the balanced diet with vitamins, minerals and protein which we (and our pets) now take for granted.

The 'aphrodisiacs' of the rich, in which the medical books of the ancient and medieval world abound, and the folk recipes of the rural poor may represent an attempt to balance their respective diets.

2. Over-population was not always a problem. Most of the early religions were concerned (and some still seem to be) with increasing population. The fertility cults had animals associated with them and often plants of various kinds. Time seems to have transmuted some of these totemic animals and sacred plants into 'aphrodisiacs'. This does not necessarily rule out the possibility that they have aphrodisiac qualities since the protracted orgies and feats of copulation which gods like Dionysus demanded of their followers made San Francisco in the early 1970s look like a quiet place.

3. Male dominated societies are very concerned with virility. Virility means succession because it produces sons. The symbol and instrument of all this is the penis: the magic wand which men have and women do not. Unfortunately the rigours of excessive endeavour – either in traditional warrior societies or in modern commerce – mean that the wand can sometimes lose its magic. Although an adjustment of priorities would have probably been sufficient to restore vigour, generations of high achievers have relied instead on quack remedies and fashionable stimulants.

The inescapable biological differences between the sexes and the natural limitations of male sexual performance are another reason for the universal interest in aphrodisiacs. In India these matters have been the subject of serious study for thousands of years which is why no book on human sexuality can ignore Hindu erotology.

4. Until the advent of modern dentistry tooth decay was a problem and with it went halitosis. Many 'aphrodisiacs' had an aromatic, astringent and even anti-septic quality evidently intended (though this was never made clear) to overcome the age-old **anaphrodisiac** of bad breath.

HOW HAS THE BOOK BEEN COMPILED?

It has been the intention to include the widest possible range of sexual postures and practices from all cultures because these are proven and established sexual stimulants and have an immediate and (in most cases) practical application.

There are some inclusions in this category which are not really practical and if that is not self-evident it is made clear. There are also warnings concerning some sexual postures (e.g. standing ones) and no-one with joint or back problems, or arthritis should attempt those positions clearly intended for supple young athletes (and often taxing even for them!)

Although inclusion of something does not indicate approval, nor exclusion disapproval, you will certainly not find anything which is cruel or 'unequal'. Reciprocity and mutuality are the essence of sex – the ideal unit is two. This conviction rather than the dangerous concept 'good taste' has governed the choice of what is included.

Dangerous plants and substances have been excluded with the exception of absinthe and Spanish Fly which are there only because people might look for them and need to be told that they are killers. The other substances included are those foods and plants which have stood the test of time, and which occur again and again as aphrodisiacs in different cultures and different periods and which may, therefore, have some property – chemical or psychological – which we do not understand.

Among the consumable aphrodisiacs are recipes and drinks which notable lovers or gourmets have concocted for their own use. These are for amusement as are the more improbable 'positions' and the ghastly cocktails of crocodile semen, panther's breath and other horrors which the exploitative have in the past persuaded the gullible to quaff (see Philtres and Potions).

There is no index to the book because that is not the way it should be used. It is designed for browsing and is extensively cross-referenced so that you can pursue a particular theme. The illustrations are a useful guide to what may interest you.

If some of the entries look strange in a book of aphrodisiacs (e.g. Chairs) it is because mundane things often have innate erotic possibilities. And if you think grandfather's old chair is being put to some unthought of uses, you may be underestimating both the chair's history and grandfather!

The book is intended to be lighthearted in tone but it also has a serious point.

If casual sex with numerous partners was ever satisfactory is doubtful – what is beyond doubt is that it is now potentially deadly with the widespread presence of the AIDS virus among both heterosexuals and homosexuals. Variety is the most potent aphrodisiac of all. It is quite possible to learn from other cultures (particularly Indian ones) all that two human beings need to know for a lifetime of sexual variety within one relationship. That is the real point of this book.

PROBLEMS

It is not within the scope of this book to deal with sexual problems which everyone has at some time. Such problems may be physical or psychological. Your doctor may or may not be trained as a sex counsellor – probably not. Ask to see one, ask for referral to a teaching hospital, persist until you are confident that you are getting the best possible advice and treatment from gynaecologist, urologist, psychiatrist or sex counsellor – depending on the problem. Do not be told that you must live with the problem: there is a fair chance that it is not true. If your GP is a barrier, consult the telephone book for self-help organizations. Sex is too important: its powerful dynamics mean that great joy when it is right, turns to abject misery when it is not. Persist.

'I shall show you a philtre
Without potions, without herbs
Without any witch's incantation.
If you wish to be loved, love.'
SENECA PARAPHRASING OVID

ABSINTHE

A banned green liquor, once made in France from wormwood, marjoram, oil of aniseed and other essential oils. Reputedly a powerful aphrodisiac, this was the drink of Verlaine, Toulouse-Lautrec and other self-destructive geniuses. Regular consumption of absinthe leads to insanity and death which is why it was finally prohibited.
(See also ALCOHOL)

ADAM and EVE

A name for the basic sexual posture; the *figura veneris prima* of the Romans: also known as the matrimonial, frontal and missionary position. Apparently it acquired its last name because the Polynesians – who prefer the squatting or Oceanic positions – concluded by discreet observation that it was the preferred method of their visitors. All lovemaking positions where both legs of one partner are within the other partner's legs (irrespective of who is on top) fall into this broad category, provided they are facing.

The fact that the couple face each other is the key to the popularity of this posture, or it should be. Each partner can read the needs and register the pleasure of the other – the essence of good lovemaking. If the man is considerably taller than the woman, the basic frontal position is less satisfactory because each cannot see the face of the other. If the man is very much larger his weight may also be a problem. If he is much smaller than his partner there is less disadvantage since he finds himself between her breasts which is fun for everybody. There are numerous variations of this posture which preserve its advantages while avoiding the problems of height-weight disparity.

Browse among the illustrations for ideas, which is the way this book is meant to be used.

AGATE

In the Middle Ages this stone was used as a talisman. It was widely believed that wearing agate – which is associated with the god Mercury – increased the sexual energy and attractiveness of its possessor.

ALCOHOL

Taken in relatively small quantities, alcohol can act as a stimulant and may help people overcome inhibitions which can hinder relaxed, enjoyable sex even in some well-established relationships. Alcohol is certainly an ingredient in many of the aphrodisiac recipes in this book, probably for that reason. Nor is there any better overture to lovemaking than a quiet dinner with wine: a Roman poet said that 'Venus is lonely without Ceres and Bacchus (food and wine)'.

However, in large quantities alcohol is a sedative and therefore a powerful anaphrodisiac or passion killer. Choose quality rather than quantity, always.
(See also ARMAGNAC; ANISE; BENEDICTINE; CALVADOS; CHAMPAGNE; CHARTREUSE; COGNAC; ESSENTIAL OILS; WINE)

AL FRESCO

Providing you have the sense of humour to overcome the occasional hazards such as a bottom covered with insect bites or discovery by a troop of scouts, sex in the open air is fun. The danger itself is stimulating for some people, while others enjoy becoming part of the natural environment in the most natural way there is.

Sex al fresco was always the ultimate intention of those elegant picnic parties recorded by Watteau and other eighteenth-century painters. Be adventurous. Take a hamper!
(See also SPONTANEITY; WATER)

ALMOND

A wide variety of aphrodisiac concoctions and recipes from many different cultures and periods feature almonds. In The Perfumed Garden Sheikh Nefzawi recommends almonds and pine kernels mixed together in thick honey and taken at bedtime on three successive nights as a way of sharpening the sexual appetite in men.

A modern gourmet recommends a soup made from powdered almonds, egg yolk, chicken stock and cream as an erotic stimulant to both sexes. Almonds also feature in Italian folk medicine as excitants.

The almond tree seems to have been associated with ancient fertility cults in the Near East including that of Cybele and her consort/son Attis in Anatolia. In the language of flowers almond blossom indicates passion.

Almonds also yield a fine oil which can be used in cooking or as a medium for massage.

(See also MASSAGE; PERFUMED GARDEN)

ANANGA-RANGA

A love manual written by the Hindu scribe Kalyana Malla in the Middle Ages. Although inferior to the much older Kama Sutra as a work of literature it contains a wealth of practical information. The author states his intention to demonstrate that one partner is sufficient for anyone: 'I have in this book shown how the husband, by varying the enjoyment of his wife, may live with her as with thirty-two different women, ever varying the enjoyment of her and rendering satiety impossible'.

Apart from an exhaustive catalogue of sexual postures to excite both partners, there is great emphasis on foreplay and wooing in the Ananga-Ranga. The author is also a shrewd observer who remarks that a woman's sexual appetite is often strongest just before and just after menstruation.

Despite its tiresome insistence on categorization, Ananga-Ranga (State of the Bodiless One) is a surprisingly modern work containing much that is relevant to a society living with the AIDS virus.

(See also EROTIC LITERATURE; INDIA)

ANAPHRODISIACS

Practices or substances which are thought to reduce or remove sexual appetite have been employed – usually by repressed males – throughout human history. The early morning cold bath once favoured by English public schools came from Ancient Rome and Greece via the Medieval monasteries together with the rest of the curriculum. In case the chilling effect wore off later in the day Galen, the second century Greek doctor, had the resourceful idea of wearing sheets of lead next to the skin. If this did not remove lust completely it must have made the execution of it extremely uncomfortable.

Cooling drinks and plants have also been used as weapons against lust. The limp lettuce favoured by monks is altogether believable but the cucumber – seriously suggested as a potent anaphrodisiac by some authorities – somehow seems to lack the right qualities.

ANCHOVY

Perhaps because they are both fish and salt – two common aphrodisiacs the world over – anchovies have a well-established reputation as a sexual stimulant.

ANILINGUS

(See *FEUILLE DE ROSE* also BOTTOMS and BUTTOCKS; *POSTILLIONAGE*)

ANISE

An umbelliferous plant indigenous to the Levant. It was mentioned by the Greek botanist Dioscorides and has long had a reputation in Europe and the Middle East as an aphrodisiac. The essential oil, anise vert, is used in perfumery. Aniseed can be used in cooking and anise is also available in a wide range of alcoholic drinks. Pernod, Ricard and Pastis from France are the most widely available, but Greek ouzo and Turkish raki are also good. The best and driest ouzo is manufactured on the island of Mytilene (Lesbos).
(See also ESSENTIAL OILS; MASSAGE; and PLATE 7)

APHRODISIACS

For those who like to categorize things, aphrodisiacs can be divided into five groupings: analogous, associative, 'cannibalistic', therapeutic and sensory. There is a sixth category which almost deserves to be a group of its own: these could be called novelties. Any new food tends to be described as 'aphrodisiac' by those eager to sell it. For no other reason were potatoes once on the list. In practice, many aphrodisiacs fall into more than one group.

Analogous aphrodisiacs resemble sexual parts in some way, e.g. ginseng; mussels.

Associative aphrodisiacs are connected with erotic activity, often in a long-forgotten way e.g. the hare is sacred to Aphrodite; sticks of bread to the fertility god Priapus (but they are also analagous of course). These relics are part of our folk inheritance.

'Cannibalistic' is a misuse of the term but it well describes the common idea that if you eat the vital organ of another animal (even if it is not another human animal) you will absorb its strength or essence in some way, e.g. rams' testicles.

Therapeutic aphrodisiacs are those substances which are thought to have a sexually stimulating effect on the body of the user, whether drunk, inhaled, eaten or applied externally. This group can be sub-divided. There are substances that create a sense of warmth (the opposite of frigid). Secondly there are substances which relieve inhibition. Thirdly there are substances which have a diuretic effect. Lastly, and most mysteriously, there are substances which may or may not replicate our own sex hormones.

Sensory aphrodisiacs include massage, erotic art, literature and performances, and sexual games and techniques which prolong, or give intensity or variety, to lovemaking.

LE SATYRE ET SA FEMME.

APPLE

This delicious fruit is as rich in symbolism and mythology as it is in vitamins (C and several of the B group) and minerals. It is the ultimate symbol of our own sexuality because it was with an apple that Adam tempted Eve. There is an ancient folk saying that if you cut an apple from top to bottom you will have revealed to you the temptation which Eve offered to Adam. How many unsuspecting maidens must have blushed when they carried out the experiment and realized that they were looking at the shape of their own vulva.

Apples, and the products of apples such as cider and the incomparable spirit Calvados, have long been thought to possess rejuvenating and aphrodisiac qualities. There is evidence that the 'food of the gods' in Norse legend, which restored vitality and youth, was apples and cider. Good quality, unsweetened apple juice is widely available and contains many of the qualities of the original fruit.

Apples were used in love magic in Europe in the Middle Ages. If a woman slept with an apple under her arm 'or some other privvy place' and in the morning persuaded a man to eat it she would become the 'apple of his eye'.
(See also ALCOHOL; SEX MAGIC)

APRICOT BRANDY

Long considered an aphrodisiac drink. In A Midsummer Night's Dream the fairies are told of the efficacy of apricot and Shakespeare seems to have been drawing on an established folk tradition. Dried apricots steeped in sweet muscat wine for a week or two are a favourite sweetmeat with which lovers can feed each other.

ARMAGNAC

Henry IV of France, whose numerous mistresses made enormous demands on him, always preceded his lovemaking with a thimble glass of Armagnac. Less widely known than Cognac this excellent brandy from Gascony has a richness and earthy quality that is all its own.
(See also ALCOHOL)

A Chinese name for the basic frontal sexual posture. In Chin P'Ing Mei, an erotic novel of the Ming Dynasty, it is called 'the oldest, fiercest game'. For urgent, uninhibited lovemaking it is probably the best position of all.
(See also CHINA; EROTIC LITERATURE)

ARS AMATORIA

Ovid's famous poems on the Art of Love were the ostensible reason for his exile from the Rome of Augustus in AD8. The real reason had more to do with politics. In Ars Amatoria he is scathing about some of the contemporary poisonous potions employed to 'compel Venus' but lists more palatable aphrodisiacs:

> *Eat the white shallots sent from Megara*
> *Or garden herbs that aphrodisiacs are,*
> *Or eggs, or honey on Hymettus flowing,*
> *Or nuts upon the sharp-leaved pine trees growing*

Ars Amatoria is a great work of literature: elegant, wise and full of psychological insight. Ovid was about fifty when he completed the work and he had been a great lover of women in every sense. Much of his no-nonsense advice is addressed to women. With a new lover he suggests 'reckon up each of your charms and take your posture according to your beauty . . . if you are especially attractive of face, then lie on your back.' Ovid discusses a large number of sexual postures and concludes (perhaps because his health was no longer robust): 'A thousand modes of love are there; and the simplest and least laborious of all is when the woman lies reclined on her right side' (i.e. spoon fashion).

Ars Amatoria is about the light-hearted enjoyment of sex. It is also about love.
(See also EROTIC LITERATURE)

ARTEMISIA

A genus of aromatic perennial herbs including Mugwort and Wormwood from which absinthe was once made.
(See ABSINTHE; MUGWORT)

ARTICHOKE

Street vendors in Paris had a special cry for this vegetable:

> *Artichokes! Artichokes!*
> *Heats the body and the spirit.*
> *Heats the genitals.*
> *Catherine de Medici liked artichokes!*

Artichokes can be eaten hot or cold but they must first be boiled for about half an hour. The fleshy base is the part you eat, pulling it off the bristly leaf with your teeth. Bland on their own, hot or cold artichokes should be served with a tangy dressing: the oil and wine vinegar base can be flavoured with some of the other reputed aphrodisiacs such as garlic and fresh coriander, or chopped capers. The dressing should be mainly oil with only a little vinegar or lemon juice. The ritual is to peal off a leaf, dip in the dressing and straight to your mouth. When all the leaves are gone, cut off the bristly cone and eat the remainder of the fleshy heart. Artichokes make an excellent and leisurely beginning to a romantic meal.

Philandering men were once said to have artichoke hearts . . . 'for every girl a leaf.'
(See also EATING and FOOD; EROTIC CUISINE)

ASANA

The term simply means 'position' and is used not only in the Sanskrit sex manuals but also in Indian dance and in Hatha-Yoga. The famous Lotus Position is an asana.

Much use is made of the word asana in describing lovemaking positions in this book because – as in yoga and dance – it implies a posture held for a time which then moves fluidly and easily into another. The whole reason for studying different positions is to give variety and a multiplicity of sensations to your lovemaking. Put together different asanas, as you would put together different foods and spices to create a meal.

(See also BANDHA; INDIA; TANTRA; YOGA)

ASPARAGUS

The Ancient Egyptians, Romans and Greeks were all fond of asparagus which was cultivated much as it is today. Although it disappeared from the European table during the Middle Ages its use was widespread in the Arab world. Sheikh Nefzawi recommends a daily dish of what sounds very much like an asparagus omelette as a powerful aphrodisiac.

The Sun King, Louis XIV, reintroduced asparagus – perhaps because of its erotic reputation – to his glittering Court at Versailles. It has always been expensive but is a delicious appetizer. It can be eaten cold but is better hot. Asparagus should be boiled upright in a bundle so that the edible tips cook in the steam. As you eat each tip, dip it into a shared bowl of melted butter, hollandaise sauce or oil and vinegar. Only the fingers should be used so that the erotic symbolism of eating asparagus can be used to the best effect.

(See also EATING and FOOD; HOPS)

ASTROLOGY

Most of the early European herbalists believed that there was some correspondence between the Zodiac and those plants which affect the human body – for example a plant dedicated to Venus was thought to affect both sexual performance and function.

Different parts of the human body were also thought to be associated with the various astrological signs. This link could be either negative or positive and can therefore be included among occult aphrodisiacs. In caressing or massaging your lover it may be useful to refer to the illustrations of astrological correspondence included in Nicolas Culpeper's original Herbal. If your lover is a Taurean it may be worth looking for erotic trigger points in the area of the neck; with a Cancerian try the breasts – if the Sun was in Scorpio when your partner was born proceed straight to the genitals!

AUBERGINE

The eggplant or aubergine is mentioned in very early Sanskrit texts and may have been a native of India. The plant came into Europe via the Arab world during the Middle Ages and is now grown in warm climates everywhere. Aubergine is a principal ingredient of the Provencal dish ratatouille which contains various other aphrodisiac plants (onions, red and green peppers, tomatoes, garlic, coriander) although no-one seems to have made the connection.

In the West Indies a dish made from aubergine, chives, pimentos, vanilla pod

and peppercorns in a white sauce was used as a sexual excitant.

The classic aubergine dish is Imam Bayildi from Turkey. The hollowed vegetable is stuffed with the same ingredients as Ratatouille (without the courgettes) and slowly simmered in olive oil for two or three hours. Usually it is eaten cold. A Turkish Imam is said to have fainted with pleasure after the women of his harem fed him the aphrodisiac dish: its name means 'fainting imam'.

AVOCADO

The Spanish conquistadores brought back the avocado pear to the Old World where its reputation as an erotic stimulant soon became well-established at the royal courts. The Aztecs called it ahuacatl which means testicle, presumably a reference to the stone rather than the entire pear, unless there was something about the Aztecs which history has failed to tell us. Many women find the sensation of eating avocado especially pleasing and the texture has been compared to semen.

BAMBOO SHOOTS

Some early Chinese writers suggested that this vegetable, eaten over a long period, had aphrodisiac effects.

BANANA

The excellent nutritional qualities of what is botanically a berry may have rather less to do with its erotic reputation than its umistakeable shape. The banana, and the closely-related plantain, were delighting the European palate and imagination as early as the sixteenth century.

BANDHA

A term meaning 'knot' which is used to describe Tantric lovemaking positions. Tantrists believe that they can channel and use sexual energy: many of the postures are analogous to electrical circuits, and are designed to contain the force within the couple.
(See also ASANA; TANTRA)

BASIL

Few herbs have as many associations with sex as basil. In the European folk tradition it was an important ingredient in many love charms; in Haitian Voodoo it is the sacred plant of the insatiable sex goddess Erzulie; and Arab writers mention it as one of the most important aphrodisiac herbs. Although none of the European herbalists speak plainly about it, there is a persistent implied suggestion that while basil inflames the passion in women it has quite the opposite effect on men. Culpeper's comment is typical: 'it helps the deficiency of Venus in one kind. So it spoils all her actions in another. I dare write no more of it.'

As a culinary herb, basil is second to none. Whenever possible use the fresh leaves, although dried basil is also useful in sauces. Tomatoes sprinkled with finely chopped basil deserve the title 'love apples' and it is hard to imagine that the dish is an anaphrodisiac for men. No doubt the garlic, pine kernels and Romano cheese which are combined with basil in olive oil to make the famous pesto sauce for pasta, more than counterbalance any anaphrodisiac effect!

Basil is also available as an essential oil and can be a fragrant additive to massage oil. In The Perfumed Garden Sheikh Nefzawi compares the delicate herb to a

woman's body, explaining that both must be rubbed softly with the fingers before there can be any pleasure.

(See also EROTIC CUISINE; ESSENTIAL OILS)

BATHING AND BATHS

Bathing is more than an important preliminary to lovemaking it is, in itself, an enjoyable sensory experience – or it should be. Immersion in water or showering involves stimulation of the largest sensory organ we possess – our skin. In addition to the sensation of the water itself, which can be soothing or exciting, there are a variety of temperature changes to be enjoyed. The act of washing, lubricated by soap or other cleansing agent, is in effect massage which is also pleasurable.

Bathing also stimulates other senses. Essential oils or perfumes added to warm water can stir every kind of association or memory, transforming the bathroom into anything from a pine forest to a bed of roses.

Bathing also involves nudity. Our own nudity, glimpsed in mirrors, may or may not excite us according to taste. The nudity of others is always potentially exciting but again is a matter of taste and will depend upon who you are in the habit of bathing with. The Romans had baths dedicated to washing and conversation, and others where sex was the main objective. The same was true in Japan and the Ottoman Empire, and is still the case with contemporary saunas. The bonhomie of a communal bath after team sport, and the intimacy of lovers sharing the same tub may be very different, but much of the sensory experience is the same – as it is when you bathe alone. We should enjoy all our baths.

Most lovers bathe together from time to time. It is rather more comfortable in a large sunken bath or a jacuzzi, but equally rewarding when someone has to lean on the taps (the compensation is having the hotter water). Showering together probably leads more often to immediate sex, not only because there is more room and showering is invigorating rather than relaxing, but because the skin tension remains better as there is no long immersion. For the same reason it is better to wait a short time after a bath before making love – if you can.

(See also ESSENTIAL OILS; PERFUME; WATER)

BAY LAUREL
(*Laurus nobilis*)

An important culinary herb which has a long association with virility. The ancient Greeks crowned successful athletes with laurel leaves; the Romans decorated victorious generals in the same way. Arab and oriental authorities maintained that its regular inclusion in a man's diet ensured victories of a different kind.

(See also ESSENTIAL OILS and WILD PLANTS for methods and precautions)

BEDS

Although much attention is paid to beds as platforms for sleeping on, their other function is often ignored. It is generally accepted that harder, more supportive mattresses are better for our backs and they also provide a better surface on which to make love. But bed height and other factors are also important.

In cultures where much of the time is traditionally spent on the floor (e.g. India, Japan) some joints will become more supple with use and some muscles more developed. Beds will also tend to be low platforms or at floor level. These are important factors to remember when studying the sexual postures of these cultures. India has more to teach us about sex than any other civilization but if many of these delights are to be accessible you must either take to the floor (and use Hatha Yoga or another regime to improve your flexibility) or give some thought to your bed. Adventurous lovers will in any case want and need to take to the floor sometimes.

The bed should be firm, with no side panels to restrict or hard edges to bruise. It should be as wide as possible and solid. Noisy beds may be amusing in a hotel

or someone else's house, but as a general rule can only lead to passion-killing inhibition unless you live in total isolation, have a hide like an elephant or feel that you have something to prove.

If anything, the bed should be high rather than low. The traditional Madame's test for selecting beds for a bordello cannot be faulted. A man of average height should be able to penetrate a woman on all fours (he standing on the floor, she kneeling on the bed) without stretching or stooping. If you are discreet it should be possible to assess your 'bedside manner' in the shop without causing too much alarm. If that works, then the bed is the right height for all other postures and activities (e.g. Wheelbarrow; Reversed Crow or Cascade; Gamahuche), which it would be rather more difficult to mime without – in the words of Lady Bracknell – 'attracting comment'.

BENEDICTINE

Although it is produced by monks, this excellent liqueur – with its carefully-guarded formula – has long had a reputation among gourmets as an aphrodisiac.
(See also ALCOHOL; ESSENTIAL OILS)

BERGAMOT

It is bergamot (Citrus bergamia) which gives Earl Grey tea its distinctive scent. A strongly feminine aroma, bergamot has been credited with the ability to excite both men and women and is an excellent addition to the bath or to massage oil.
(See also BATHING AND BATHS; ESSENTIAL OILS; MASSAGE)

BIRD FINDING NEST

A Chinese sexual posture in which the woman reclines on a table or high platform with her legs raised. Her partner supports her legs and moves in long strokes, erratically at first and almost completely withdrawing, very gradually working towards shorter strokes and a regular rhythm.

Black Bee

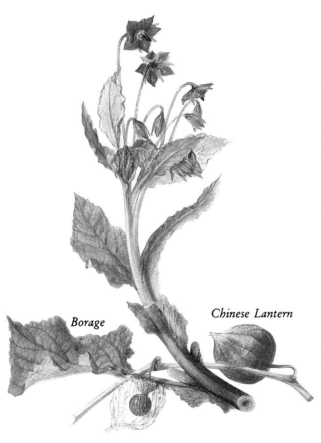

Borage *Chinese Lantern*

PLATE 1

26

BIRDS'S NEST SOUP

This oriental delicacy is made from the nests of swallows which yield a gelatinous substance which is then flavoured with other ingredients and spices. Traditionally the Chinese regard bird's nest soup as a powerful aphrodisiac.

BLACK BEE

One of the classic Indian lovemaking positions translated here from the Ananga-Ranga: 'If you lie flat, with your lover astride you, her feet drawn up and her hips revolving so that your penis circles deep within her sex. it is *Bhramara*, the black bee.'

In China this popular posture has the delightful name of 'Shouting Monkey'.

BLACKBERRY (See DEWBERRY)

BONE MARROW

This highly nutritious substance appears regularly in aphrodisiac recipes from most times and cultures. The poet Horace records that its use as an erotic stimulant was widespread in Rome during his time (the first century BC).

BORAGE

Pliny called this beautiful herb 'Euphrosinum' and styled it 'Ego borago gaudia semper ago' which means 'I, Borage, bring joy always.' The young leaves of borage can be eaten in salads and its madonna blue star-shaped flowers added to long drinks or frozen singly in ice cubes. Most of the great herbalists refer to borage as an erotic stimulant. Gerard wrote: 'the leaves and flowers of borage put into wine make men and women glad and merry, driving away all sadness, dullness and melancholy.'

BORDELLOS

The reason for including an entry on places where you are more likely to find lack of self-esteen and despair than Susie Wong and happiness is that some of the trade practices and skills employed in traditional bordellos are of considerable interest. Although most 'houses of ill repute' are very far from being human and well-run places, a few are and always have been. A guide compiled in the same manner as the myriad which now report on restaurants worldwide would probably indicate much the same incidence of mediocrity and flair (and if the food guides ever concerned themselves with waiters and kitchen staff, similar amounts of exploitation and misery).

As with restaurants only a few bordellos have ever achieved real immortality through excellence. In the East the 'flower boats' of nineteenth-century Canton, and the exquisite 'green houses' of Japan's Yoshiwara ('floating world') are legendary. In the West, eighteenth-century London had the lavish Pantheon and 'Mary Wilson's' which catered for women. In the early twentieth century the Chicago club run by the indefatigable Everleigh Sisters (not to be confused with the Brothers) was world famous as was Polly Adler's New York 'Mansion' in the 1920s. Pre-war Paris had the only Western bordello which paid homage to the superior erotic legacy of the East. This was the Akropolis near the Opera, which had a Chinese salon, a Desert Room, as well as Persian and Turkish chambers. In each the sexual confectionery was as genuine as the decor.

The traditional working furniture of Western bordellos – chairs and mirrors – are dealt with elsewhere, as are beds. There are also entries on the erotic art and literature which have always been available in the best establishments in both East and West. Massage is also dealt with elsewhere, as is masturbation both as a performing art and as a learning technique. All mainstream sexual practices warrant individual entries. A bordello trick which might be omitted if not included here is where the woman rides the man and at the right 'dramatic' moment covers his head with her knickers effectively blindfolding him. Although it suffers more than most sexual techniques from sounding absurd in cold blood, the mixture of cassolette and the dissociation techniques used for more sinister purposes, produces an almost delerious orgasm in some men which has made it a favourite bordello trick since time immemorial.

(See also CASSOLETTE; COURTESAN)

BOTTOMS AND BUTTOCKS

As a visual aphrodisiac, a man's bottom is of almost equal interest to a woman as her buttocks are to him. Women will tend to value neatness and compactness whereas roundness and ampleness are the qualities more likely to excite a man. As with so much of our sexual behaviour (some would say most) this is an inheritance from our primate ancestors for whom buttocks were the primary sexual stimulus. In The Naked Ape, Desmond Morris suggests that as Man evolved and became more upright, female breasts enlarged to replace buttocks as the primary focus – there being no mechanical reason for them being much larger in female humans. As a result we can now enjoy both.

Although bottoms are less sensitive than breasts they are an important erogenous zone in both men and women. The perineal area below the buttocks and between the legs, (from anus to testicles in men and anus to vulva in women) is often ignored but extremely sensitive. In Tantra this is the seat of Kundalini, the almost limitless sexual energy waiting for release within each of us. Caress or massage are ways of stimulating this forgotten area, as are most of the rear-entry positions.

The anus itself is sensitive but a taboo area for some people and for others not. Freud is amusing on the subject: 'I hope I shall not be accused of partisanship when I assert that people who account for this disgust by saying that the organ in question serves the function and comes into contact with excrement . . . are not much more to the point than hysterical girls who account for their disgust of the male genital by saying that it serves to void urine.'
(See also *FEUILLE DE ROSE; POSTILLIONAGE;* TANTRA)

Durum and Soft Wheats

PLATE 2

28

BOUILLABAISSE

The wonderful fish soup from Marseilles which contains a wide variety of fish and shellfish depending on availability. Venus herself is said to have created the recipe in order to stimulate the fire god Vulcan to some suitably volcanic lovemaking. Certainly Apuleis attempted to seduce a Roman widow with a spicy fish stew in the second century AD. Very similar dishes have the same erotic reputation in India and other parts of the world.
(See also EATING AND FOOD; EROTIC CUISINE; SEAFOOD)

BREAD AND BAKING

French bread is a descendant of the penis-shaped loaves baked and consumed as part of phallus worship in the Pre-Christian period. In ancient Syracuse vulva-shaped bread was more popular, as it was among the German-speaking people of the North.

Interestingly, bread is rich in vitamin E which is associated with fertility. The worshippers of Ceres, goddess of the harvest, and other fertility deities, ate the sacramental bread of their gods and copulated in the newly-planted fields to encourage the fecundity of the grain crop. The custom is still practised in some pre-industrial societies and vestiges of it were reported in Europe as late as the nineteenth century.

It is not surprising that bread and baking have aphrodisiac connotations. Contemporary New York confectioners who produce outrageously erotic cakes are carrying on a tradition dating back to the Stone Age.
(See also PHALLUS; SEX MAGIC)

Breasts and Nipples

The sucking of nipples as foreplay – or as an end in itself since some women can have an intense orgasm from this alone – is a reminder of how the urges and memories of infancy and childhood continue to resonate in our sexual behaviour.

Men also enjoy having their nipples sucked. There is nothing effeminate about it, or abnormal either on the part of the sucker or the sucked. Men's nipples are erectile and well-served with nerves. They offer additional sensory possibilities for both partners, a fact sometimes overlooked by women.

Far more often overlooked, and with far less excuse, is the enormous importance of breasts to women. Not only does the sucking, nibbling and palming of a woman's nipples and the gentle kneading of her breasts create a complicated and profound psychological response in which sexual and maternal instincts are all mixed up, there is a magical – but very real – connection between her nipples and her clitoris.

The importance of breast stimulation for women cannot be exaggerated. The best method of stimulation is to imitate, or remember, the actions a child makes when sucking. Not all lovemaking should be gentle, but this aspect of it always should. Aggressive 'maleness' will destroy the special mood and the pleasure. As a general rule men should spend longer stimulating the breasts of their lover. When her need is too urgent, or you have outstayed your welcome, you will soon be directed elsewhere.

(See also *Pearl Necklace*; Pregnancy and Lactation)

L'ATTAQUE VIGOUREUSE.

Bride Cakes and Wedding Food

Apart from the cakes which form part of the wedding feast in a great many cultures and are remnants of ancient fertility cults (see Bread and Baking) there are some foods given to the bride and groom which are specifically intended as aphrodisiacs to ensure that despite their bashfulness the wedding night is all it should be. In many European countries in the middle ages the couple were given highly-spiced 'bride cakes' soaked in alcohol before going to bed.

Nuts of all kind, especially chestnuts and hazelnuts, were another popular wedding night stimulant. In France a soup containing chervil and tarragon is still popular in some regions. An aphrodisiac specifically intended for the bride consisted of bruised marigold petals in a glass of mead.

(See also Alcohol; Chestnut; Hazelnut; Honey)

BURNET
(Sanguisorba minor)

The Salad Burnet rather than the Great Burnet (sanguisorba officinalis) enjoys a good reputation as a general stimulant with some aphrodisiac qualities. The leaves and young shoots should be gathered in the spring before flowering and eaten in salads or added to soups. They can also be added to wine or brandy. Before the advent of the hop burnet was often used to flavour beer.

(See WILD PLANTS for methods and precautions)

BUTTERFLY KISS

A technique of using the eyelashes to stimulate sensitive parts of the body such as nipples or upper lip and philtrum. Not for those who have short eyelashes or cannot blink rapidly. As it is in fact the minute hairs on the surface of the skin which are stimulated, feathers can be a useful substitute.

(See also FEATHERS; PATTES D'ARAIGNEES)

CALVADOS

The perfumed brandy made from Normandy apples. Good calvados is the drink of the gods; ordinary calvados is often more palatable than other inexpensive brandies derived from the grape. The mythology and symbolism surrounding apples probably account for the supposed aphrodisiac qualities of calvados, although drinking it is a sensuous experience in itself. Applejack is also a spirit made from apples but the quality is far more variable (especially as some of it is home-made in remote areas) and ranges from very good to poisonous.
(See also ALCOHOL; APPLE)

CANTHARIDES (See SPANISH FLY)

CAPER

The piquant flower buds of the trailing shrub *Capparis Spinosa* have been used in sauces and pickles for a very long time. They have always been considered a strong aphrodisiac and are even referred to in the Bible: 'and the caperberry shall fail' (Ecclesiastes).

The green flecks in Sauce Tartare should be chopped capers, although regrettably gherkin, which is cheaper, is often substituted. Beaton's recipe for caper sauce has never been bettered.

CAPTIVE POSITION

An orgasm-delaying posture where the man controls all the action – unless of course his partner is a *Kabbazah* or 'holder'.
(See *KABBAZAH*)

CARAWAY

These pungent seeds are an ingredient in numerous oriental aphrodisiac concoctions. The Greek healer Dioscorides believed in their erotic properties as did Shakespeare's old reprobate Falstaff: 'in an arbour we will eat a last pippin of my own grafting with a dish of caraways . . . and then to bed!'

CARDAMON

The crushed seed pods of cardamon mixed with ginger and cinnamon, and sprinkled over a salad of boiled onions and peas, is an aphrodisiac recipe which appears in

Captive Position

several Arab texts. Cardamon is also an important ingredient in Indian cuisine.

Chewing cardamon after spicy food which your partner has not shared (especially if it contained garlic) is a cure for the anaphrodisiac of bad breath.

Cardamon is also available as an essential oil. Its clear spicy notes are more masculine than feminine – add a few drops to the base oil if you are massaging him. (See also ESSENTIAL OILS; MASSAGE)

CARROT

John Gerard was only one of numerous herbalists who have recommended the carrot as helping in 'love matters'. Perhaps because of its phallic shape and fierce colour the Greeks called the vegetable 'philtron'. Although low in protein, carrots contain carotene which converts to vitamin A, as well as B1, C and E.

A popular Arab recipe was to stew carrots in milk. Taken regularly this dish was thought to improve both sexual appetite and performance.

CASCADE

This term is often used to describe all the standing inverted postures but is in fact the standing variant of soixante-neuf. As he is likely to be the supporting partner, it is better for the man to concentrate on giving the woman the intense sensation of an orgasm enjoyed upside-down and forget about his own pleasure. Unless exceptionally well-matched in size mutual kissing in this position is likely to be difficult and is not, in any case, very satisfactory for the man.

Do not attempt this position unless you are both fit. It is better to initiate it when the woman is already strongly aroused and close to orgasm. Stand by the bed with your legs on either side of her upturned face: lean forward and pick her up. (See also CROW; SOIXANTE-NEUF; *DU BARRIE*)

CASSOLETTE

The most powerful weapon in a woman's sexual armoury – her own natural perfume. Each individual has her own scent – an aroma which is unique to her. It is a combination of the different scents of her hair, genitals, armpits, and indeed every part of her skin. It is never offensive unless she does not wash regularly or is unwell.

Some men have a more developed olfactory sense than others, but all of them consciously or unconsciously respond to what the French have termed a woman's cassolette. If a woman's natural perfume was indeed a weapon it would have one hundred per cent accuracy over a very long range. It is also infinitely more sophisticated than the weapons of war since it will only strike those who need to be struck – i.e. sexually 'mature' heterosexual males.

Many believe that this system of unseen and usually unconscious sexual signalling which is our animal inheritance, may be an important component in passionate love – the sometimes unaccountable attraction which can destroy homes and topple thrones. Perhaps it is just as well for the stability of society that most women destroy their own precious cassolette with the overuse of deodorants and harsh artificial perfumes. A vast and persuasive industry encourages women to replace their natural scent with the 'pong' of aluminium chloride or thinly-veiled antiseptics.

The so-called 'intimate' deodorants which have a place for occasional use are the ultimate passion killer.

None of this argues against the use of perfume which is a time-honoured and important aphrodisiac. The skill lies in choosing one which reacts well with your own cassolette and complements and enhances it. Mild armpit deodorants should be used in the same way. If you are worried about excessive odour there is no substitute for regular and thorough washing.

Much of this also applies to men – especially the importance of washing. They also have a natural scent of course which women react to sexually. But it is relatively crude and simple – a woman either likes it or not. It has none of the allure and magic of a woman's cassolette.

(See also PERFUME; SENSE OF SMELL)

Celery,

Celeriac

Parsley

PLATE 3

CAVIAR

The eggs of sturgeon: very scarce, extremely expensive and never to be confused with lumpfish eggs or other substitutes. Caviar should be eaten with thin toast. It can be eaten with scrambled eggs to make more of it but a single mouthful of the unadulterated thing is really to be preferred. The traditional drink with caviar is iced vodka, although champagne is very good as well.

The idea that fish eggs are aphrodisiac is very old. Caviar's special reputation probably dates only from the Belle Epoque.
(See also EATING and FOOD; SEAFOOD)

CELERY

History records in some detail the erotic stimulants and aphrodisiac foods which the Marquise de Pompadour persuaded Louis XV to take. Some of them seem to have worked – certainly she was his favourite among many mistresses – but whether her celery soup was among the successful foods is not recorded.

The ancient Greeks regarded celery so highly that they used it in the same way as laurel, making wreaths to decorate the heads of successful athletes. It is interesting that both plants have long been regarded as aphrodisiacs.

Both common celery and the root form celeriac are rich in iron, vitamins and mineral salts.

CHAIRS

No room in a well-equipped, traditional bordello was considered fully furnished unless it contained a low chair. Certain sexual positions are only possible with the support of a chair, a fact not lost on Joseph von Sternberg when he directed Marlene Dietrich in The Blue Angel.

Lovemaking chairs should be squat and narrow so that the woman can comfortably straddle both the chair and the man sitting on it. Upholstery is optional, but there should, of course, be no arms. A high back for support and to hold on to can be useful, but above all the chair must be sturdy.

Chairs and stools widen the sexual repertoire for stiff-jointed Westerners in the way that a well-chosen bed does. All the positions are worth experimenting with but should be varied and tried in sequence. In all positions the woman sits on the man.
1. She sits on his lap facing him. This gives excellent clitoral stimulation and face to face contact. She can either milk him with her sex if she has that skill, or rock to and fro.
2. From the same position she draws her knees up while he circles her in his arms to support and move her. This gives very deep penetration.
3. This is position (l) reversed, i.e. she faces away. Her breasts are more accessible for caress but she or he must manually stimulate her clitoris.
4. This is position (2) reversed
5. She faces him and straddles him standing on the floor. She can now rise and fall or vary the movement by gyrating her hips. She should drop to position (1) for

34

better clitoral stimulation, quicker movements as orgasm approaches – or when her legs become tired!

6. As position (5) but reversed with the additional visual stimulus for him that she can arch her back to show off her buttocks or bend over forward.

The principal advantages of chair positions are the strong clitoral stimulation for her, especially in (1); and the powerful visual aphrodisiac for him of seeing his lover and her sex moving up and down on his penis. The visual excitement for both partners can be enhanced by placing the chair next to a tall mirror.
(See also MIRROR)

CHAMPAGNE

The uniquely romantic associations of champagne – which is always chosen to mark a special occasion – are almost certainly the reason some people credit it with aphrodisiac qualities. But that does not mean that it does not work.

Champagne is expensive because the genuine process is labour intensive. The bubbles give strong stimulation to the tongue and palate which many people find pleasurable. The carbon dioxide also means that the alcohol reaches the blood stream more quickly.

The best and driest champagne is Blanc de Blanc which is made exclusively from Chardonnay grapes. For a very special occasion try rosé champagne where the grape skins of a black grape variety lend it a pink tinge.

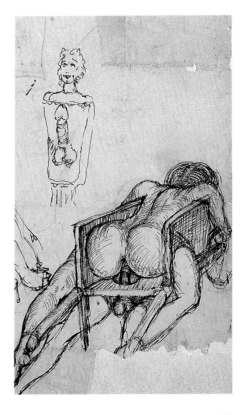

Less expensive but excellent are the sparkling white wines of Saumur or Spanish Cava. Both are produced in the time-honoured method.

CHARMS (See SEX MAGIC)

CHARTREUSE

Both the green and yellow versions of this famous liqueur (which like Benedictine is made by monks) have been said to have aphrodisiac qualities. Green Chartreuse in particular is reputed to excite women.
(See also ALCOHOL; ESSENTIAL OILS)

CHEESE

Those hard cheeses which are less pungent to the nose but have a strong, salty flavour are those most often regarded as aphrodisiacs. Chief among these is Parmesan which can be grated over food, melted or eaten in splinters with a pear.

CHERRIES

There is archaeological evidence that cherries were cultivated in Egypt as early as the seventh century BC. Many different varieties were known by both the Romans and the Greeks. Their wonderful taste (cherries are about ten per cent sugar) and appearance, their convenient size and pleasing roundness have always made them the ideal fruit for lovers.

Cherry brandies are also popular. The best known are Kirsch, Ratafia and Maraschino.
(See also ALCOHOL)

CHERVIL (See BRIDE CAKES and WEDDING FOOD)

CHESTNUT

This wonderfully versatile food can be eaten in many different ways. They can be freshly roasted: in which case buy them from the street vendors who can still be found in European cities as autumn turns into winter; or they can be purchased in candied form from expensive shops as marron glacés.

Chestnuts are an ingredient in many different aphrodisiac recipes. The ideal lover's dessert is Mont Blanc. Simply whip chestnut purée (tinned unless you are very conscientious) with brandy and serve it in a glass with a pile of whipped cream on top.

CHICK PEAS

Sheikh Nefzawi, author of The Perfumed Garden, maintains that the following recipe is an infallible sexual stimulant for men: Honey and onion juice are heated until the onion evaporates. This is then mixed with a paste made from pulverized chick peas and taken at bedtime in the winter. Why it should be 'in the winter' is not made clear, but presumably he felt that the passions were more likely to need stirring on a chilly night.
(See also PERFUMED GARDEN)

CHINA

Until the communist revolution – China was ordered and governed according to the elaborate rules of Confucianism which above all valued dignity and restraint. Although this might be expected to have had a repressive effect on sexual expression the Chinese have always been a pragmatic people. There were also several features of Chinese society which tended to increase rather than diminish interest in sexual matters: polygamy, the widespread toleration of prostitution, and the existence of a class which had both wealth and leisure.

Although there was a revival in the nineteenth century, the most important periods for erotic art and literature were the cosmopolitan Tang (AD 618 to 906) and the Ming which finally collapsed in 1644. Sex manuals had been produced in China from the earliest times but those of the Ming which are built upon all the earlier wisdom have most to teach us. Many of the sexual techniques in this book are from the love manuals of the Ming.

Two famous novels of the Ming period give us a clear idea of attitudes both towards sex and sex manuals. In both The Prayer Mat of Flesh, and Golden Lotus the principal characters regularly use erotica. Golden Lotus herself insists on experimenting with new postures and techniques detailed in an erotic scroll. Hua Chen, a sexually sophisticated woman in The Prayer Mat of Flesh maintains that to create the right mood for lovemaking a man and women should study erotic albums together until 'she is moist and he is erect'.

The Chinese erotic tradition included an elaborate pharmacopoeia of sexual stimulants and an arsenal of sex toys. But for all that sophistication, and despite the evocative names they give to sexual positions, the woman is never the equal of the man. All in all China has less to teach the West about sex than India.
(See also EROTIC ART; EROTIC LITERATURE; SEX TOYS)

CHOCOLATE

Originally a drink sacred to the Aztec fertility goddess Xochiquetzal. The first European to taste chocolate was the conquistador Cortez at the Court of Montezuma. As with many exotic foods imported from the New World, chocolate was hailed as an aphrodisiac. The reputation persisted and by the seventeenth century monks in France were prohibited from consuming the inflammatory substance. At the time of Louis XIV chocolate sweets became very popular in the French Court. If a lady accepted one from the Sun King himself it indicated that he had invited her to his bed – and she had accepted. Boxes of chocolates are used in the courtship rituals of our own times.
(See also VANILLA)

CHURNING CURDS

The Hindu love manual Panchasayaka describes this asana: 'Caging your lover in your arms, you part her knees and sink into her, crushing her body to yours: this is known as Dadhyataka, or Churning Curds'.

Churning Curds

CICADA FIXED TO A TREE

A rear-entry lovemaking posture where the man lifts his partner's hips as he thrusts into her.

CINDER SIFTING

A descriptive name for the special way of moving a woman can use when she is riding a man. It defies explanation, but think of moving your hips around once or twice and ending with a series of little jumps – just as you would separate the ash from the cinders in a sieve. The French called this 'la diligence de Lyon' after the jerky ride which travellers in horse-drawn mail coaches once experienced. A technique worth perfecting and much easier than learning to be a Kabbazah if you were not born with the ability.
(See KABBAZAH)

CINNAMON

This much prized spice is obtained from the bark of a tree which is now cultivated throughout the tropics. For thousands of years it has been regarded as an aphrodisiac and was one of the valuable products which were brought along the spice roads. The name cinnamon means 'fragrant plant of China'.
(See also ESSENTIAL OILS)

CLAWS OF THE DRAGON

A Chinese sexual position where the woman bends over a high couch or table. It is described in Chin P'ing Mei: 'In the game called Claws of the Dragon, Hsi-Men could look down and see red enter white, hard enter soft. Again and again in the game whose end is dreaded and yet longed for, the pattern was repeated: until Purple Fire Lady, noisy from both mouths, suddenly became quiet and turned her autumn-glancing eyes to him'.

CLIMATE AND TEMPERATURE

In his 'Problems' – the archetypal question and answer book – Aristotle asks: 'Why are men in winter, but women in summer, more impelled to venery?' Hesiod, reflecting on the same problem in 'Work and Days' wrote: 'in the season of tiring summer . . . kids are fattest, wine is most mellow, and women are most lustful – but men are feeblest'.

Many of the novels written about the British Empire allude to the same phenomenon: heat has an aphrodisiac effect on women but tends to have an anaphrodisiac effect on men.

CLITORIS

A Latin word meaning 'shutter' which refers to the fact that in many women a hood of skin analogous to the foreskin needs to be pulled back to expose this tiny organ. So much has been written about the clitoris – stressing its vital role in sexual pleasure for women – that many men tend to proceed straight to it in foreplay as if the clitoris were a 'start' button on a piece of machinery.

Tantrists have a rather better understanding of female sexual response. Tantra maintains that the upper lip, the nipples and the clitoris are joined together and should be stimulated in turn with kissing and sucking.

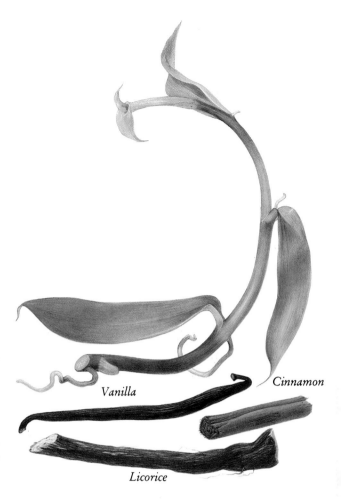

Vanilla

Cinnamon

Licorice

PLATE 4

Another name which the Roman writers gave the clitoris was naviculus or 'little boat'. Two thousands years later a similar association was made by whoever coined the charming lesbian slang term 'boy in the boat'.
(See also MASTURBATION; TANTRA)

CLOTHING AND FASHION

Clothes are worn to protect our bodies from heat, cold or friction – the Chairman
Mao suit is an example of 'clothes'. Everything else – tailoring, colour, surface,
embellishment – must be regarded as 'fashion' and the purpose of fashion is sexual
attraction, or ritual – or some combination of the two. Part of sexual attraction is

the desire to identify – honestly or dishonestly – with a group likely to be attractive to those we wish to attract (e.g. Hell's Angels; Business Executives). Within our category we dress according to our culture, our finances and the extent to which we are concerned with attracting others. Our 'dressing pattern' is also dictated by our gender, how we see our own sexuality and how we wish it to be perceived.

Sexual fashions tend to work toward similar goals in all times and all cultures. Men emphasize and exaggerate their genitals: tight jeans and pouched briefs fulfill the same function as Renaissance cod pieces or the penis sheaths worn by some tribal peoples. A Victorian lady emphasized her buttocks with a bustle while a femme fatale of the 1950s wore a short tight skirt and high heels which turned her bottom into a sort of sexual mobile which was compulsive viewing for any male.

Other sexual characteristics attractive to the opposite sex are emphasized in a variety of different ways. Male fashions stress broad shoulders, flat stomachs and neat buttocks. Female fashions stress breasts and legs.

Not all aspects of fashion are as obvious as this. Severe, angular clothing may emphasize the femininity of a woman. A silk 'Latin lover' shirt with full sleeves may emphasize a muscular male torso.

Even less obvious are the 'borrowed' fashions such as fur, feathers and leather. If you can only achieve orgasm wearing a skin-tight leather suit you have a fetish. If your partner is the same, he or she has a fetish. But if leather makes someone feel sexy and attractive, and is not an end in itself, then it is fun and interesting and everything that fashion should be.

Many fashionable prostitutes have an impeccable sense of how to use clothes to their best, aphrodisiac effect. They have never abandoned stockings and suspender belts for tights, or if they have it is for the sort which leave pubis and bottom naked. They do not wear knickers if they feel like it: who is to know except someone you want to know? And he is likely to be excited by the knowledge. The daring nature of the experiment might also excite you, as well as avoiding a 'knicker line' and making your bottom look sexier. Wear silk knickers for special occasions – they hold your scent better. Finally a nipple spied occasionally is sexier than a nipple constantly on view. If your pigmentation is light a little lipstick helps. If the dress fabric and design show contours, tweak your nipples to perk them up when you go to the powder room. He will notice.

COBRA

This sexual posture is from the Hindu Panchasayaka: 'If, lying with her face turned away, the fawn-eyed girl offers you her buttocks and your penis enters the house of love, this is Nagabandha, the coupling of the Cobra'. The Chinese and Japanese equivalent is called 'Mandarin Ducks'.

COBRA HOOD

In this asana the man's hands are clasped behind the woman's back; one of her legs is hooked over one of his arms. A position for those whose joints are supple from exercise or Hatha Yoga.

42

COBRA KNOT

The Chinese of the Ming Dynasty called this position 'Turning Dragon'. Pillows under the woman's bottom make it more practicable. If she rolls over onto her back it becomes the fully-pressed position with exceptionally deep penetration: in which case her lover should control his thrusts carefully to avoid hurting her.

COCONUT

Both the milk and the flesh of coconuts have been said to act as an erotic stimulant when taken over a long period. Roasted flakes of coconut makes an excellent additive to muesli.

A missionary in the South Pacific (who had a problem in more than one sense) attempted to ban the consumption of coconuts on the grounds that they incited lustful behaviour and 'looked like giant testicles.'

Coconut oil can be used as a massage medium.
(See MASSAGE)

Cobra Knot

43

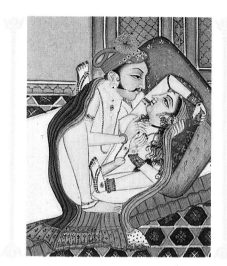
Con

COGNAC

A ninteenth-century aphrodisiac drink consisted of yolk of eggs and a pinch of paprika stirred into a glass of cognac.

CONCH

An Indian love text from the sixteenth century describes this asana: 'When she lifts her thighs and you sit astraddle them, your knees tightly clamped, kissing her tenderly and riding saddle upon her buttocks, this is SHANKHA, the Conch'.

CONDOMS

Sex with a condom is not as good as sex without one, but for many people there is no satisfactory alternative either as a contraceptive or to reduce the possibility of contracting AIDS. Imaginative manufacturers have responded by giving condoms additional features: it is now possible to buy condoms in most colours (including black); they can also be ribbed, studded or shaped to vary the sensation for both partners. Condoms themselves tend to reduce sensitivity which is a positive advantage for men who have problems with early orgasm, but some have anaesthetic at the tip which is designed to enhance this effect. Most imaginative of all manufacturers are the Jiffi company who have managed to make these essential but rather unappealing items fun: their range includes fruit flavoured condoms and luminous ones which glow in the dark.

If condoms are part of your sex life it is important to make a ritual out of their use. Ideally the woman should fit it for her lover and make it part of her foreplay. Masturbate him to maximum erection, grip the teat between your fingers to expel the air (some have no teat) and unroll it down the shaft with your other hand. Maintain manual stimulation until penetration.

CORIANDER

The seeds and leaves of this delicious herb are both edible and were widely believed to be aphrodisiac. Albertus Magnus, the thirteenth-century occultist, believed that this effect was enhanced if the plant were picked in the last quarter of the moon. Try the crushed seeds with baked apple and sprinkle the chopped leaves on salads, ratatouille and hot, spicy dishes.

Coriander also yields an essential oil which is used in the manufacture of Eau de Cologne and can be added to massage oil.
(See also ESSENTIAL OILS; MASSAGE)

COSMETICS AND BODY PAINTING

Decoration of the face and body is a universal human urge. A woman redoing her lipstick in the powder room of The Ritz is part of a tradition which includes cicatrization, tattooing, and elaborate body painting as well as face make-up. The reasons for body decoration can be religious, ceremonial, or decorative – which means sexual.

The actual process of decoration, and the subsequent tactile and visual enjoyment of it, is part of the skin eroticism of some peoples. Many of the tribal peoples of central India regard tattoo marks on the women as a powerful sexual stimulant. Although all forms of body decoration were once used by both sexes, the only generally accepted decoration for men in Western cultures now is the tattoo and that is not widespread.

Apart from the dark pigments used to accentuate eyes, red is the most useful colour in the palette of women's make-up. Red lips are a powerful sexual signal. Even used on the nails, red still finds a strong response. In the late eighteenth century, when low necklines and see-through shifts were fashionable, women extended their make-up to their nipples – also red of course. Since the 1960s the practice, like the nipple, has reappeared from time to time.

It is not perhaps a facial make-up which too many women would feel happy with – except perhaps in a highly modified form – but a very pale face with strongly defined eyes and intensely red lips finds a strong erotic response in many men. This is the face of the Shakti, the female principle in Tantra, and the archetypal female mask in Japanese Noh. Taken to extremes, this make-up can of course become reminiscent of the female protagonists in vampire movies – but some men find them sexy!

Body painting sometimes features in Tantric ritual

COURTESANS

One of the ancient writers mentions an epitaph he saw on a tombstone: 'I was a courtesan in the city of Byzantium. I am Kallirrhoe, experienced in all the arts of voluptuousness'. There have always been prostitutes but they have not always been

victims as they often are in our society. The hetaerae of ancient Greece were well-educated and respected with an aspect of the love goddess devoted to them, Aphrodite Pandemos.

Japanese courtesans. the oirans, were given the same careful education as geishas.

Their sexual education – as seems to have been the case universally – was made by secret observation of more experienced courtesans with their customers.

Much of the information in this book is culled from records of the skills of courtesans in different societies who made sexuality an art form. In France courtesans socialized with kings, and sometimes married them. Perhaps the greatest of them all was Ninon de Lenclos (1620–1705) – generous, intellectual (or so Molière thought) and outrageous. To the end of her days Ninon felt it her mission to instruct young men in the skills of love. It pleased her, and after more than five thousand lovers she had much information to impart. We even have the recipe for Ninon's favourite aphrodisiac soup: 'Mix a pureé of fresh peas with a consommé. Add a glass of fino sherry and a little lemon juice. Just before serving pour in champagne, and when it is before your lover a spoonful of whipped cream'.

CRESS

The Romans made much of cress as an aphrodisiac, calling it 'impudens' which means 'shameless'. Apicius, a cookery writer, created a stimulating drink from onion water, pine kernels, cress and pepper. The physician Marcellus Empiricus made an aphrodisiac salad with the same ingredients, adding a pinch of lavender. It is not clear whether these writers were referring to Bitter Hairy Cress (illustrated), Watercress or Garden Cress. They are all of the Cruciferae family and have some properties in common – so this may not be important.

Rocket

Cress

Horseradish

PLATE 5

CROSS DRESSING

In the old joke an English peeress returns home unexpectedly and finds the butler in her bedroom. 'Take off my shoes James; now remove my dress; undo my brassiere' . . . This part of the story can be protracted but the punchline is: 'And don't let me ever catch you wearing my clothes again!'

Some men and women enjoy dressing in the clothes of the opposite sex, finding it amusing to explore gender differences and self-image in this way. This explains the popularity of fancy dress parties: note how often the most masculine men go as women – and usually as tarts so that they can use the most extreme feminine signalling in clothes and make-up.

At this level – as a lighthearted sexual game – cross-dressing does not imply transvestism or homosexuality.

(See also CLOTHES and FASHION; COSMETICS and BODY PAINTING; SAME SEX RELATIONSHIPS)

CROSSING THE MOUNTAINS WITH FIRE

A Chinese rear-entry lovemaking technique where a series of quick short thrusts is followed by long slow thrusts and so on.

CROUPADE

The traditional French term for all buttock or rear-entry sexual postures whether the woman is standing, bending, kneeling or lying flat. Only if one leg is between another – or straddling – does it become 'cuissade' or half-rear entry.

Some people do not like these positions because they find them 'animal'. Others like them for the same reason (See the *Deer* position). If a croupade position is to be taken through to orgasm, he or she will probably have to stimulate her clitoris manually. Although some women find that the stimulation of the perineum (the area between anus and vulva) more than compensates.

CROW

The Indian equivalent of *soixante-neuf*. Unless you are exceptionally well-matched it is better to take turns in kissing each other. The man should remember that she will be guarding her teeth with her lips and stretching her mouth wide open which is tiring. The women should remember that if she is on top he will soon have a stiff neck. The variant of the Crow where the couple lie on their sides is more comfortable for some people.

CRUSHING SPICES

A posture for the protraction of lovemaking. He kisses her breasts and caresses her while she moves on him (or holds him if she is a *kabbazah)*. In China this is called 'Cranes with Necks Entwined'.
(See also KABBAZAH)

CUBEB

A berry similar to pepper and once used as a condiment. The Chinese valued cubeb as an aphrodisiac as did the thirteenth-century Arab physician Avicenna. His recipe was powdered cubeb mixed with honey.

CUISSADE

The half-rear entry lovemaking postures, from the French 'cuisse' meaning thigh. This group of postures includes simple variants of rear entry (croupade) where the legs are straddled but also the 'spoon position' where she lies on her side and he takes her from behind. (The spoon position is likely to be cuissade, but for the

Crushing Spices

technically minded if his legs are together and his knees fit exactly into hers it would be a croupade position).

─────────────── CUMIN ───────────────

A spice widely used in aphrodisiac cuisine, especially in the Middle East. It is also available as a pungent essential oil.
(See ESSENTIAL OILS)

─────────── CUNNILINGUS (See GAMAHUCHE) ───────────

─────────────── CUPID'S FLAG ───────────────

A technique where the man stimulates the vulva and clitoris with the tip of his penis for some time before penetration. Sometimes useful when premature ejaculation is a problem.

─────────────── CURVED KNOT ───────────────

A sexual position from the Tantric tradition. The lovers are linked together in every possible way in a bandha which allows them to enjoy each other and to postpone orgasm for as long as they wish.
(See also *BANDHA*; TANTRA)

Curved Knot

─────────────── DANCE ───────────────

When we dance we become more than ourselves: in that, and in many other respects, dance is like sex at its very best. Academics have written a great deal about what is probably the oldest human art but Isadora Duncan explained it better: ' . . . I feel the presence of a mighty power within me which listens to the music and then reaches out through my body . . . sometimes it raged and shook me until my heart nearly burst from its passion!'

Her description is strikingly similar to the ecstatic state which is the object of the sexual practices in Tantra. And of course the great Hindu god Shiva, the male principal, is Lord of the Dance. He created the world out of his dancing and will one day destroy it in the same way.

Dance has as many facets as sex, and many of them correspond. Salome's Dance of the Seven Veils, the ancient Greek Cordax, and good striptease, are all aphrodisiacs. Disco dancing is a more stylized form of sexual display. Much traditional ballroom dancing is gentle courtship, whereas the polka and the more energetic

forms of modern dancing are closer to foreplay. And, like sex, dance at its best can be an expression of love.

(See also MUSIC; PERFORMING ARTS)

DATES

A sadly underrated food. For many people in Africa and the Middle East dates are the staple food. The fruit contains vitamins A, B, C and D and approximately as many calories per hundred grams as beefsteak. Some writers have included dates themselves in aphrodisiac recipes, but 'palm wine' which is made by fermenting juice tapped from the crown of the tree, is reported to have embarrassed some male travellers by its immediate effect on their anatomy.

DEEP THROAT (See IRRUMATIO)

DEER

A posture described in the Hindu love manual Five Arrows: 'If your lustful lover buries her face in the pillow and goes on all fours like an animal, and you rut upon her from behind as though you were a wild beast, this coupling is Harina, the deer'.

LE SATYRE
FAILLISSANT.

DEWBERRY

One of various species of bramble which are generally grouped together as 'blackberry' (Rubus fruticosus). The dewberry comes earlier than most blackberries which is an important distinction since dewberries are thought to be a sexual stimulant in some English rural communities. But all blackberries found after the end of September are said to 'belong to the Devil' who sometimes takes delight in reversing the effect.

DILDO

These artificial penises are included because they are not only used as substitutes but also in foreplay and for display. The motif of a woman using one is a common image in erotic art and is obviously exciting to some men.

Shakespeare refers to dildos and the dissolute Earl of Rochester ('not sober from one year end to the next') wrote poems about them and even imported them. The ancient manufacturing centre for 'olisbos' was at Miletus in Asia Minor. From the late Middle Ages Italy became the major producer in the West. The dildo has also been called a 'godemiche'; in Japan the word is 'harigata'.
(See also SEX TOYS)

DILL

This herb is often associated with fish, which has tended to increase its reputation as an aphrodisiac (see SEAFOOD). But dill is also considered an aphrodisiac in its own right, especially among gypsies. Both seeds and shoots can be used in a wide variety of ways.

DISTILLATE OF LOVE

The old name for the clear, slippery substance secreted by glands surrounding the urethra, which seeps from the penis during the earlier stages of sexual excitement. More plentiful in some men than in others it can be a useful lubricant in some foreplay games and in masturbation. Distillate of Love has also been used in magic potions to cure frigidity. Sheikh Nefzawi in The Perfumed Garden writes cleverly about this aspect of male physiology: 'As soon as it stands it begins to weep; if it sees a pretty face, it weeps; if it touches a woman, it weeps. It even at times weeps tears of remembrance'. Although Distillate of Love precedes male ejaculation it often contains sperms and can, therefore, cause pregnancy.

Dog

DOG

As with all croupade positions the woman enjoys stimulation of the perineum (the sensitive area between the vulva and anus) but may need additional attention paid to her clitoris if she is to achieve orgasm.

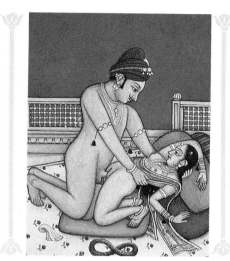

Dolita

DOLITA

The name of this asana means 'swing' because for the woman the internal sensations are said to be similar to those experienced while swinging.
(See also SWINGS)

DREAMS AND FANTASY

All of us use fantasy in our sex lives: we can pleasurably imagine or recall sexual situations when engaged in something else; or while masturbating or making love we can fix strongly stimulating images in our minds.

In Kama Sutra there is a description of 'transferred love' which is the practice of making love to one person while thinking of another. No doubt beds everywhere are more crowded than is ever suspected: film stars and rock idols are probably kept most busy, but all of us will make the odd nocturnal visit to someone else's bed quite innocently on our part.

There is no need for any feelings of guilt about having these fantasies. Each of us carries more psychological baggage than any airline would ever accept. These half-remembered thoughts, memories and daydreams are us, they are part of the person who gets into bed. And while making love (to another who has a similar but different collection of psychological baggage) anything can be dislodged and fall out of the suitcase, from a passing lust for a film star to a major obsession. Sex is nature's own therapy as well as being many other things.

Dreams (the kind we have while sleeping) are less within our control and are often forgotten on waking. For this reason some lovers keep a sort of dream diary as a means of tuning-in to each other's fantasies, with the idea that this makes their lovemaking more imaginative. These games can be useful and enjoyable, but if you find these explorations of your unconscious disturbing you should discontinue the practice or in cases of real distress seek the advice of a psychiatrist.

DU BARRIE

In this sexual posture the woman assumes a head or shoulder stand – supported against the side of the bed, possibly on cushions – and her partner steps over her, penetrating her from a standing position. Additional clitoral stimulation with her partner's thumb will be necessary but many women find an orgasm in this inverted position particularly intense.

The origins of this position and its name are obscure but a Folklorist records that an enterprizing cooper, who manufactured clothes pegs from the offcuts of his trade, took inspiration from the way that two pegs fit together and named his erotic discovery after the most notorious courtesan of the day.

DURIAN

This large and extremely pungent tropical fruit is a prized and expensive delicacy in Indonesia and Singapore. Its aphrodisiac properties are legendary but many people find the aroma of Durian unbearable and it is not permitted on aircraft or public transport. Like it or loathe it: once tasted, Durian is never forgotten!

Ears and Earlobes

The erotic possibilities of ears and their sensitive lobes are often ignored. An early Japanese manual recommends stimulation of the outer ear and canal with a pointed tongue, slowly following the outer convolutions before plunging into the centre. It is better to hold your breath while doing this or you will sound like a hot air balloon which is getting painfully close.

Freud regarded compulsive earlobe tugging (your own) as a substitute for masturbation. In fact some women can climax simply by having their lobes sucked and nibbled. The heavier type of pendant earring is as much concerned with stimulating the ear and neck as with fashion and display.

Eating and Food

This entry is not concerned with recipes but with the physical and social business of eating and drinking. There is a very old saying that 'if you want to know the way a person is in bed, watch them eat.' A disturbing observation for the primly over-fastidious; the messily gluttonous, or those who attend to their own plate but ignore the needs of others! Eating and sex are equally important to the survival of the species, which is why they are such strong drives with a large amount of pleasure attached to them. It is quite logical to see how a person approaches a sensual pleasure pursued in public in order to deduce their approach to one which in our culture seldom is.

Eating, like sex, should be enjoyed. Of course every meal cannot be a major production. Everyone has to eat the occasional sandwich standing at a railway station, but the quick event can be enjoyable too (as can the hurried sexual event between stations).

At every opportunity make the most of a meal. It is not by accident that the vocabulary of both food and sex is full of French words. They understand that both create an opportunity for ritual, drama and of course sensual pleasure. The physical act of eating is intensely pleasurable: lips and tongue are stimulated, as are taste buds and the sense of smell. Dining also provides tactile and visual pleasure. Gourmets might argue about it, but the delights of the table are only exceeded by those of the bed. Whenever possible let the one follow the other – but not too precipitately, and try not to over-indulge in the first pleasure in case it affects the second.
(See also ALCOHOL; EROTIC CUISINE)

Elephant

EGG

Arab erotology makes much of eggs as an aphrodisiac. In most of the recipes they are strongly spiced with pepper and sometimes cinnamon.

Eggs and brandy whipped together with milk, honey and a pinch of salt to make an egg flip has acquired a twentieth-century reputation as a sexual stimulant.

ELEPHANT

A rear entry asana where the woman arches her back, while her lover moves in her with a slow, insistent rhythm.
(See *CROUPADE*)

ENTWINED

A flanquette posture with straddled legs. Excellent for clitoral stimulation, especially if her middle is thrust forward by a supporting cushion.

EROTIC ART

Sexually inspired images – such as the so-called 'Venus of Willendorf' of around 30,000 BC – are among the earliest evidence of human culture. By the period 2000 to 1500 BC the variety of sexual postures depicted in the art of Mesopotamia and Egypt suggests that the artists (and therefore their patrons) had a sophisticated interest in the pleasures of sex as well as in rituals associated with fertility.

By the late Greek period there is no longer any possibility of misinterpreting the artist's intention. Superbly painted Attic vases, cups and bowls – often given as gifts to courtesans – depict every kind of sexual pleasure. This is fully-fledged erotic art, designed to celebrate sexuality and to instruct and inspire those who look at it.

Roman erotic art did not approach the quality achieved by the Greeks, but there is a cheerful vitality about the numerous amulets, charms and figures (where they have survived) reflecting the Roman preoccupation with the phallus which was influenced by both Greeks and Etruscans. The murals from the Pompeii brothel, which are purely aphrodisiac in intention, have a naive charm all of their own.

After the Fall of Rome, Europe had to wait for the Renaissance before artists could explore erotic themes more openly. Even then female nudes were usually 'Venus', males 'David'. Such incidents from Classical mythology as 'Leda and the Swan' were also popular as were biblical episodes like 'Susannah and the Elders'. Woe betide those who flouted this convention or overstepped the mark. Raphael's gifted pupil Giulio Romano had to flee after his drawings honestly depicting lovemaking positions were engraved and published as illustrations to Aretino's sonnets.

The same essentially hypocritical attitude has prevailed in Western art up to the present time. Some artists concerned with erotic themes had the fortune to be born during periods of greater enlightenment: (Rowlandson, Klimt) others not. Many artists – and many great ones including Raphael, Rembrandt, Goya and Turner – still managed to deal with erotic subjects. Eduard Fuchs said: 'Art has treated erotic themes at almost all periods, because eroticism lies at the root of all human life'.

Entwined

Tourists who have spotted the carving of a couple happily engaged in 'soixante-neuf' in Toledo cathedral will know that sex, like love, usually finds a way.

The East – notably India and Japan – has produced considerably more erotic art than the West. China experienced repeated waves of censorship over a very long period and although Chinese landscape painting is sublime (and rich in erotic symbolism) little of the erotic art compares with that of India or Japan.

In Hinduism sex is sacred, it is the animating principle within everything. The Judaeo-Christian idea that sex is something to feel guilty about is incomprehensible to a Hindu. Consequently India has by far the richest tradition of erotic art in the world. From the very earliest times the sub-continent has produced an infinite variety of art: in the stone and wood carving of its temples; in its bronzes, and in its many schools of painting.

If Indian erotic art is the most varied and sublime any civilization has produced, then the shunga, or erotic print, of Japan is certainly the fiercest. Japanese erotic art has no religious meaning and no purpose beyond the celebration of sexual pleasure. The use of perspective, the strong line, the patterned fabrics, the exaggerated genitals – everything works towards the creation of an image which is intended to be strongly aphrodisiac.

(See also CHINA; INDIA; JAPAN)

─────────────── EROTIC CUISINE ───────────────

Those with a serious interest in aphrodisiac cooking should consult La Cucina dell'Amore (Omero Rompini, Catania, 1926); La Table et L'Amour (M.E. Saillard,

Paris, 1950) and Venus in the Kitchen (Norman Douglas, London, 1952). Between them the books cover the two great European gastronomic traditions as well as including some interesting dishes from around the world.

Other individuals have made their contribution to the subject, especially courtesans. The splendid, if expensive, soup devised by Ninon Lenclos is included in the entry on courtesans. Madame du Barry also experimented with aphrodisiac cooking after the death of the Marquise de Pompadour. The dishes with which she attempted to excite Louis XV included a soup of shrimps in chicken stock flavoured with dill; Capon stuffed with chestnut purée, and an omelette containing tiny pieces of fresh ginger.

EROTIC LITERATURE

Books about sex can be divided into two broad categories: instructional and descriptive.

The instructional books all have the same general aim which is to help people get more from sex. This can be achieved in a variety of ways. Some of our contemporary manuals begin from the premise that people have sexual problems and set out to solve these based on the techniques of sex counselling. The Hindu love manuals were written out of religious conviction: by imparting knowledge they attempted to give sex its rightful place in the scheme of things. In his excellent 'Joy of Sex' and its sequel – to which all subsequent Western books on the subject (including this one) owe a considerable debt – Alex Comfort has roughly the same intention as the Hindu writers but in place of religious conviction is a desire to brush away cobwebs such as inhibition and guilt. He also gives sound advice on choosing instructional books about sex, which is to avoid those written 'by non-playing coaches'.

The descriptive category consists of novels, short stories and satires, and poetry. Erotic writing of this kind is either good or bad, but it is also either erotic or pornographic. It is a very difficult area, with no absolute rules, but some distinctions can be made between erotica and pornography – it is not simply a matter of good or bad pornography.

If a book is concerned with one particular sexual activity to the exclusion of all others, if it is violent or cruel and involves subjection, if it is bleak in tone, then it is pornography. If the subject of a book happens to be sex, then it is erotica.

This is not an argument for banning pornography although most people would have no compunction in banning some of it, especially if its production involves cruelty or subjection. On the other hand who would be mean-minded enough to ban a book on, say, rubber fetishism which is not going to harm anyone but presumably gives pleasure to rubber fetishists?

Not enough is known about pornography and its effects and more research is needed as a matter or urgency. In the meantime those who would ban all books dealing openly with sex create a corresponding body of opinion which says that nothing should be banned. This could mean – and in countries where there are no restrictions may already – that some corrosively evil material is published.

The history of erotic literature from the Classical period to the present follows

58

the same pattern as the visual arts (see EROTIC ART). While Giulio Romano fled to Mantua for illustrating his sonnets, Pietro Aretino fled to Venice. Aretino was an important figure in the history of literature: a huge man with huge appetites and a talent to match. His sonnets and other erotic work were no more than a celebration of his favourite activity after making political mischief.

Just as major artists produced erotic work so did many important literary figures. Among these were Shakespeare, Donne, Oscar Wilde, James Joyce and of course D.H. Lawrence.

(See also ANANGA-RANGA; CHINA; JAPAN; KAMA SUTRA; PERFUMED GARDEN; PILLOW BOOKS)

EROTIC TRIGGER POINTS (See MASSAGE)

ERYNGO

The roots of this plant, which resemble testicles in shape, have been regarded as an aphrodisiac from very early times. In seventeenth-century England the demand for eryngos became so fierce that an apothecary named Burton opened a factory in Colchester to process them. John Dryden describes libertines:

> 'Who lewdly dancing at a midnight ball
> For hot eryngos and fat oysters call.'

Eryngo – which is also known as Sea Holly – was also eaten in candied sweets or pulverised, mixed with egg yolk and stirred into a glass of Madeira.
(See WILD PLANTS for methods and precautions)

ESSENTIAL OILS

These substances, whose original function is not yet understood, occur naturally within approximately two thousand of the quarter of a million known flowering plants. From the very earliest times essential oils, which are extracted from plants in a variety of different ways, have been used in the manufacture of perfume. These are the 'notes' which a perfumer blends together to make a perfume.

Essential oils are now generally available and it is pleasant to experiment with the wide range of different aromas by adding a few drops to a bath or to an unperfumed massage oil. But even when they are derived from culinary plants **NEVER USE ESSENTIAL OILS IN COOKING.** Essential oils are highly concentrated and powerful substances: for example Oil of Thyme is an antiseptic ten times more powerful than carbolic acid. Therefore you should **NEVER PUT UNDILUTED ESSENTIAL OILS ON YOUR SKIN.**

Never use more than one drop of essential oil per millilitre of massage oil. Always mix the essential oil with the base oil before applying to the skin. If you are subject to allergies try your chosen massage preparation on a small area of skin to see if you experience any reaction. This will normally occur within 24 hours. In the bath the maximum number of drops is four, which should be added to the hot water after it has been run, and mixed into the water to break-up the droplets. Always follow additional instructions which appear on the bottle.

Those aromas which perfumers have traditionally regarded as exciting for women are Jasmine, Rose Bulgar and more recently Ylang-Ylang. Men respond better to Vetifer, Sandalwood or Mace. These are the stimulants. For gently relaxing, women should try a few drops of Fennel in a hot bath.

(See also MASSAGE; PERFUME AND SCENT; ROSE BULGAR; SENSE OF SMELL)

EXERCISE

It is now widely accepted that regular exercise is essential to good health, which is in turn important if you are to have a good sexual appetite and enjoyable sex.

There are also certain exercises specifically designed to improve your sex life. It is interesting that those recommended for women in the Tantric tradition are strikingly similar to the 'Kegel Exercises' pioneered by Dr. Alfred Kegel and now widely accepted by gynaecologists as a means of helping to prevent prolapse of the womb and associated problems. Tantrists also believe that these exercises increase the strength of a woman's orgasm and – in time – can enable her to grip her partner's penis, a much-prized ability. The basic exercise is very simple and consists of repeatedly contracting and relaxing the vaginal muscles.

In Tantric Yoga this is often combined with clenching and unclenching the buttock muscles (gluteus maximus) in the old ballet strengthening exercise. Male Tantrists also exercise in this way. Both men and women can combine buttock clenching with outward groin thrusts simulating the movements of sex.

All these exercises have a sound medical basis. The Kegel exercise is of particular value to women and can be done anywhere at any time. Tantric groin thrusts are however liable to misinterpretation and are not recommended for the office or while waiting for buses.

(See also KABBAZAH)

EYES

Looks given and received by our most eloquent means of expression after speech can be so powerful that nineteenth-century scientists conducted experiments to see if an electrical charge was involved. The 'look of love' is one of the most effective aphrodisiacs of all.

FAME

Although it is not entirely clear in the painting, in the *Fame* position the woman sits on a stool. A more solid support such as a table is in fact preferable.

FASOLADA

The Greek version of the spiced bean soup which is eaten all around the Mediterranean in the winter months. Similar dishes are made elsewhere, notably the island of Jersey where the famous 'baked bean' is said to originate. Various types of white

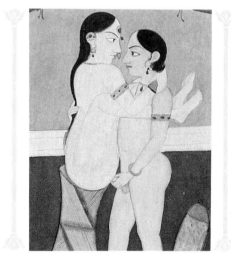

Fame

bean are used in a thick sauce which in more recent times often contains tomato. Improbably, beans have long been regarded as a sexual stimulant. St. Jerome forbade nuns to eat beans because of the widespread belief that they 'excited the genitals' of women.

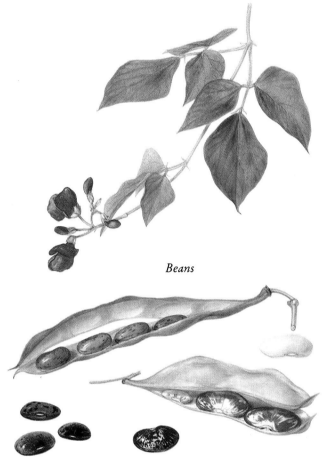

Beans

PLATE 6

FEATHERS

Courtesans, and other professional makers of love, often used feathers for stimulation. Nipples, clitoris, anus and penis were given most attention, usually with the stiffer and more pointed varieties of feather.

FEET

In the West the erotic possibilities of feet are rather ignored. Oriental erotic massage often begins with the feet which is immensely relaxing as well as pleasurable. Experience from tickling will tell you where the nerve endings are (an estimated seventy thousand of them!) and also that the massaging movements should be slow and firm.

Toes should be gently tugged individually to relieve tension and can be sucked – a practice called 'shrimping' in America. This is so pleasurable that some women

can achieve orgasm without receiving any other stimulation.
(See also *FOOTSIE*; MASSAGE)

––––––––––––––––––––––––––––––––– FELLATIO –––––––––––––––––––––––––––––––––

The most generally-used term for the practice of sucking and exciting the penis
with the mouth. Fellatio can be used in foreplay to excite your partner or as a
different ways of making love in which case his ejaculation is usually taken in the
mouth. Some women like to swallow semen, some do not. It is not obligatory and
his ejaculation can equally well be used dramatically to spray over your breasts or

elsewhere. Men attach value to their semen, so if you do take it in your mouth but do not wish to swallow, dispose of it discreetly. (No harm can come from swallowing the semen of your long-term partner but remember that it carries the AIDS virus in infected people. Avoid all oral-genital contact if you are not sure.)

Fellatio is as old as the human race and is regularly depicted in the erotic art of all cultures. The later Indian love manuals give it particular attention, for example the Ratiratnapradipika: 'Her mouth quickens now upon the shaft; when you stir to her lips and tongue tip, she swallows it as deeply as she can and kisses when you cry out: this is Sangara, Swallowed Up'.

Most lovers soon find their preferred method. As with all lovemaking, talk about it. And if he is shy ask him whether he would like you to do anything differently. Remember that it is the tonguing and mouthing of the penis which is important and not suction – although sucking sounds are an aphrodisiac for many men.

The majority of women keep their head relatively still and masturbate the shaft of the penis while sucking – some like to move their head up and down, but this becomes difficult for the quicker strokes as orgasm approaches. Newcomers should remember to keep their teeth well clear of the sensitive glans.

Most uninhibited lovers enjoy oral sex, but there are no rules except to do what pleases you and your partner. Guilt has no place in bed.
(See also GAMAHUCHE; IRRUMATIO; *JADE FLUTE*)

––––––––––––––– FENNEL –––––––––––––––

This fragrant plant was used as an aphrodisiac throughout the ancient world. In India the fennel was squeezed and the juice mixed with milk, honey and liquorice. Around the Mediterranean, fennel soup was a popular aphrodisiac.

In European folk tradition, fennel is often associated with the vulva. Many women find a few drops of the essential oil in their bath soothing.
(See also ESSENTIAL OILS)

––––––––––––––– FENUGREEK –––––––––––––––

In Bohemia and Moravia these fragrant seeds (together with lovage) were sewn into a sachet and worn between the breasts as a love charm. In the harems of the Ottoman Empire fenugreek was thought to enlarge the breasts.

––––––––––––––– *FEUILLE DE ROSE* –––––––––––––––

Literally 'rose petal', the French term for tickling your lover's anus with the tip of your tongue in foreplay or as part of oral techniques.
(See also BOTTOMS and BUTTOCKS; POSTILLIONAGE)

––––––––––––––– FIG –––––––––––––––

This sweet fruit has a complicated relationship with human sexuality. In modern Greece the word for fig is slang for homosexual; in ancient Greece it was one of the prescribed foods at the Dionysian orgies and the favourite offering to Priapus, the phallic god of physical love. Figs were eaten at traditional Chinese wedding feasts and have a widespread reputation as aphrodisiacs wherever they are grown.

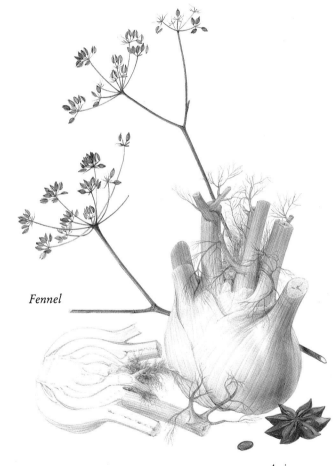

Fennel

Anise

PLATE 7

65

Postillionage (see also Feuille de Rose)

FISH (See SEAFOOD)

FISH

The man assumes the Lotus Position; when he rolls onto his back the couple will be joined in the *Fish* asana. Only for those skilled in Hatha Yoga.

FLAME FACE

In this asana the woman lies on her side and raises her leg so that her lover can enter her. When full penetration is achieved it becomes a cuissade position.

FLANQUETTE

This group of sexual positions is the frontal equivalent of cuissade. The legs of the couple overlap.

FLORENTINE

In both circumcised and uncircumcised men the strength (and speed of attaining) orgasm can be greatly increased if his partner takes up all the slack skin of the penis and holds it tight at the root while he moves in and out of her.

Flame Face

FLOWERS

The traditional and best gift for a woman from her lover. The natural fragrance of some flowers has also been credited with aphrodisiac powers by different herbalists and writers. The list of flowers said to excite women includes gardenia, frangipani, lily of the valley, night-scented stock and tobacco plant.
(See also ESSENTIAL OILS; SENSE OF SMELL)

FOOTSIE

An under-the-table game which lovers sometimes play. The excitement can be intensified by other factors such as risk, and intimacy shared but concealed. Physically, *footsie* can range from discreet nudges, to shoeless caressing of the legs or even direct genital masturbation with the toes. (Long nails on either hands or feet are a considerable disadvantage sexually).
(See also FEET)

FOOT YOKE

The Chinese equivalent of this asana is called *Pawing Horse*

FREQUENCY

Sex itself is an aphrodisiac. If you make love frequently you look better and sleep better – which helps to keep your sexual activity at a high level. It has also been suggested that frequency maintains sexual hormones at a high level. Regular sex will certainly mean that you have a good chance of remaining sexually active well into old age. Forget old wives tales – old wives can still have an enjoyable sex life.

FROG'S LEGS

Still a delicacy in French cuisine of course, and much prized by the Romans as an aphrodisiac.
(See also EATING AND FOOD; EROTIC CUISINE)

GALLOPING HORSE

The famous Chinese lovemaking position. The man begins by kneeling and holding his partner's thighs, as their passion increases and the pace quickens he falls forward onto her.

GAMAHUCHE

Also called cunnilingus. This is the technique of exciting a woman's sex with lips and tongue. Gamahuche can be foreplay or an alternative to genital lovemaking. A more important sexual skill than fellatio because of differences in a woman's response, but try to enjoy both.

As usual, the man should proceed more slowly than he will want to. Open her legs gently, kiss the sensitive insides of her thighs. Start near her knees and move up slowly. When you have opened her do not go straight to her clitoris. Vary where you kiss and how you kiss. Use your tongue like the infinitely variable and sensitive thing it is rather than an electric drill attachment which only has one action.

If you think you are overdoing the slowness of your approach – ask her. If you think he is too slow – tell him, or push his head where you want it.

End with lapping at her clitoris as a cat laps its milk. Do not begin by doing that.

Some women are inhibited about being kissed. With persistence and understanding this can be overcome. As with many things, one success will usually lead to others. Many women enjoy having their nipples manipulated while being kissed in this way. He really needs both hands where he is: you should have no inhibitions about caressing your own nipples.

(See also BREASTS AND NIPPLES; FELLATIO)

Goat

GAME

Duck, pheasant, partridge, venison, hare – in fact all game appears regularly in aphrodisiac cookery. This may have to do with the strong aromas and tastes involved or the fact that many of the animals have forgotten associations with ancient fertility deities. For example the hare was sacred to Aphrodite.

(See also EATING AND FOOD; EROTIC CUISINE)

GARLIC

Universally valued as an aphrodisiac, garlic is an essential feature in most of the world's culinary traditions. The Chinese were using garlic both in cooking and medicine two thousand years' ago. The Egyptians considered the plant sacred and garlic cloves were found in the tomb of Tutankhamun. In ancient Greece athletes chewed garlic for vitality before the Olympic games and Pliny recommended crushed garlic and coriander in white wine as an infallible sexual stimulant.

There are only two things which amorous cooks need to remember: add garlic late in the cooking or it becomes bitter, and both of you have some.

(See PLATE 14)

GINGER

This deliciously hot and tangy spice is a native of India, where it has always been important in cooking. Ginger's virtues as an aphrodisiac were recorded in many of the early works on medicine, especially in China and the Arab world. The courtesan

Ginger
(and Rhubarb)

Nutmeg

PLATE 8

Madame du Barry used ginger omelettes to inflame the passions of Louis XV. Whenever possible use fresh ginger in cooking.
(See also Essential Oils)

GINSENG

Once known only in China and Korea, the mandrake-like root of *Panax ginseng* is now available the world over. Among a wide range of other benefits which are claimed for ginseng is its ability to stimulate the sexual appetite in both men and women. It is available in a variety of forms which includes an infusion for tea.
(See also China)

GOAT

The woman should be well-supported by cushions in this lovemaking asana so that she can rise to meet each thrust of her lover's penis.

GOOSE

Perhaps because the bird was sacred to the phallic god Priapus, goose has appeared in many aphrodisiac recipes – usually accompanied by a highly-spiced sauce. Its reputation is not improved by its use in English slang to describe an uninvited and unexpected lunge under someone's clothes in imitation of a farmyard goose.

GRAPES

Always associated with the Greek fertility deity Dionysus, grapes were eaten during the wild orgies held in his honour. The Roman equivalent, Bacchus, was also identified with grapes and wine. Grapes are very nutritious. In addition to glucose and fructose they are rich in vitamin C and B especially in the lighter-skinned varieties. They also contain quantities of iron, sodium, potassium, calcium, magnesium and phosphorous.

The most delicious and sensuous dessert grapes are the different varieties of muscatel grown in various parts of the world.

GREECE

Although the necessity for moderation is a recurring theme in the writings of the Greek philosophers, sexuality had none of the associations with 'guilt' and 'sin' which characterise Judaeo-Christian civilization. In his 'History of Animals' Aristotle anticipates Desmond Morris's brilliant 'Naked Ape' by several thousand years, regarding it as self-evident that there is something to be learned from studying what is clearly common ground between animals and man.

In Greek drama (especially that of Aristophanes), art and religion, sex was accorded its rightful, central, place. But it is interesting that sexuality as an aspect of human activity was not isolated: there is no word for it on its own. Michel Foucault observes that every sexual practice had its own word, but 'sexuality' as a category did not. Aphrodisia – the acts of Aphrodite – include not only sex but all those things which give us pleasure of a similar kind: perfume; colour; shape; taste; the arts.

HAIR

Most of the human body is covered with hair: it has an infinite number of erotic possibilities. The minute, unseen hairs on the smooth areas of our skin are the

74

sensory conductors which make stroking and light massage so pleasurable. Stroking of the head hair is also pleasing, especially for women. Long hair can be brushed or lightly tugged; but the most exquisite sensations in both sexes come from caressing the fine downy hair on the neck.

Hair is also a scent trap and disperser. Head hair is particularly important, but so are genital and armpit hair. In very hot climates it has often been the practice for both sexes to shave body hair, and in some but not all Western cultures it is fashionable for women to shave their armpits. All depilation reduces the cassolette effect in women and disarms a potentially deadly erotic weapon (see CASSOLETTE).

Hair fashion and styling, with all its related products and services, is a vast industry. It follows the same patterns of change as clothing fashions for much the same reasons: the related goals of more effective aphrodisiac quality and greater profit. Hair has a powerful visual impact both negatively and positively. Some women find shaven male heads sexy; some men are excited by the look (and feel)

of shaven vulvas. Beards are attractive for some women and repel others: a strong negative reaction may be connected with attitudes towards sexuality since facial hair and lips are analogous to the female genitals.

The triangle of a woman's pubic hair is a very stimulating visual signal for men. The fashion for removing underarm tufts means that millions of opportunities for potentially aphrodisiac display are lost every day, since underarm hair is both consciously and unconsciously associated with pubic hair.

Western culture tends to exaggerate the importance of head hair to the exclusion of its other manifestations on the human body. (This was not always so. During periods when head wigs were fashionable so were pubic wigs for women.) This fragment from an Afghan poem shows better understanding of the complex erotic possibilities of hair:

'Last night my kisses drowned in the softness of black hair,
And my kisses like bees went plundering the softness of black hair.
Last night my hands were thrust in the mystery of black hair,
And my kisses like bees went plundering the sweetness of pomegranites'.

(See also CASSOLETTE; CLOTHING AND FASHION)

HARE

Supposedly aphrodisiac – as is most game – and traditionally identified with the love goddess Aphrodite.

HAZELNUT

Many nuts are considered to be sexual stimulants. Gathering hazelnuts in traditional rural communities in Europe was closely associated with sex and going 'a-nutting' in England was a euphemism for fornicating. This may be a relic of forgotten fertility rituals or it could be that the gathering of 'filberts' (on St. Philbert's Day in August) was simply an opportunity for young men and women to go into the woods together.

HOMOSEXUAL (See SAME SEX RELATIONSHIPS)

HONEY

In all cultures where aphrodisiacs have been popular, honey has been among the most frequently used ingredients. Galen – the Greek physician of the Roman emperor Marcus Aurelius – recommended 'honey at bedtime' as a sexual stimulant. The medieval Arab doctor Avicenna prescribed honey mixed with ginger and a little pepper.

Other products of honey have been used as aphrodisiacs. Marigold petals steeped in mead was a popular aphrodisiac drink among the Anglo-Saxons as was 'honey wine' which was traditionally taken by newly-wed couples for a month after their marriage and is the origin of 'honeymoon'. Attila the Hun – whom we had always suspected of over-compensating – drank so much honey wine at his wedding that he died.

Honey is easily digested and therefore an excellent source of immediate energy. It is also rich in vitamins and minerals. Traditionally the best honey comes from Hymettus, the mountain near Athens, where it has been collected since ancient times. To this day Hymettus honey is scented with flowers and heady with wild thyme.

Honey has also been used as an interesting 'anointment' in oral sexual practices and as a means of achieving better friction in lovemaking at those times when the woman may be lubricating heavily.
(See also THYME)

—————————————————— HONEYSUCKLE ——————————————————

The unmistakable scent of honeysuckle is said to be sexually exciting for women. In folk magic lonely maidens were advised to place a sprig of honeysuckle under their pillow to induce erotic and prophetic dreams.
(See also SEX MAGIC)

—————————————————————— HOPS ——————————————————————

In addition to its use as a flavouring in beer, this widely-dispersed plant can also be eaten as a vegetable by boiling the young shoots in water like asparagus.

The aphrodisiac reputation of hops applies only to women. Although its most famous product, beer, is one of the bastions of machismo in some cultures the hop has a well-attested estrogenic action. When consumed in very large quantities hops have a feminizing and anaphrodisiac effect.
(See also ALCOHOL and PLATE 13)

—————————————————————— HORSE —————————————————————

The idea that horse-riding is sexually stimulating is not simply a male fantasy: it is a well-documented fact which also happens to be the subject of male fantasy. Female anatomy is obviously better suited to direct stimulation by riding but sitting in a saddle also stimulates the male perineum.

Horses also offer a range of other erotic stimuli. It is no accident that 'riding' is a sexual term: the rhythms and attitudes are strongly suggestive. Breeches are necessarily tight and usually pale in colour. When combined with the most erotic of all colour signals – red (as in hunting pink) – they constitute a mating display which the most outré bird might envy.

Horses themselves are visually exciting. Reduced to its components – prominent buttocks, sleek surface, long hair, swinging gait – a horse has many of the features associated with a sexually-attractive woman. The enthusiasm with which racegoers visit the paddock is as much to do with aesthetics as the arcana of gambling.

Horses are also sexual 'symbols' for women. They are powerful and elegant. In horse cultures of all periods (Aryans, Normans etc.) an intimate relationship, working at many different levels, developed between horse and human. The Arab Sheikh Nefzawi recommends watching horses mate as a powerful aphrodisiac. The Borgia Pope, Alexander VI, is said to have seduced Lucretzia, his daughter, after a similar display at the Vatican.

The early Sanskrit poet Mayura left an intriguing fragment: 'You went to bathe in the river, and I took new interest in the king's stallion. He roared for the quick mares to be brought to him, he drummed with his forelegs upon them. Oh woman moist with a boy's love!'

HORSERADISH

Culinary and medicinal use has been made of this perennial herb since the first millenium BC. The Greeks valued it as an aphrodisiac; the Romans included it in the spicy sauces which they served with both fish and meat.

Dried or pre-prepared horseradish does not compare with the natural root which is now becoming more widely available. Grated into thick cream or yoghurt with a little vinegar and a pinch of salt it makes an excellent sauce for either beef or smoked and pickled fish. Combined with a tomato and wine vinegar base it makes the best possible dip for large prawns. Sprinkle chopped coriander on top for both taste and 'aphrodisiac' value.

(See PLATE 5)

HYACINTH

Generally included with those flowers whose perfume is said to excite women, the phallic hyacinth has quite different associations in Greek mythology. The beautiful young man Hyacinth was accidentally killed by his boisterous lover the god Apollo. In his grief he turned the boy into a flower which would eternally echo his beauty.
(See also PERFUME AND SCENT; SENSE OF SMELL)

Hyacinth
(Grape)

Leek

PLATE 9

INDIA

In Hinduism – the ancient religion of India and begetter of many others, including Buddhism – sex is holy. Making love is a sacrament, the re-enactment of the divine love of Shiva (Male; Death; Time; Creator and Destroyer) and Shakti (Female; Consciousness; Bliss; Energy) in her most beautiful form – Parvati, Daughter of the Mountains. Clearly the idea that there is anything shameful about sex is not only alien to Indian thought but almost incomprehensible. Insofar as the Judaeo-Christian concept of guilt is understood, it approaches sacrilege and represents a denial of all that is most holy in us.

Out of this attitude grew the oral tradition of Tantra, which warrants its own entry, and a vast body of literature concerned with sexuality and pleasure within the context of Hinduism. The oldest of these 'love teachings' is Kama Sutra, written by the sage Vatsyayana in the first century AD but drawing on many much older sources. Numerous other manuals have been written since then and translations from many of them apppear throughout this book.

As useful as all this accumulated wisdom is at a practical level, there is a greater message within all the Indian love teachings. This is that men and women are eternally complementary and equal; (this is especially true of Tantra) with the corollary that any system or practice which denies this is a distortion.

(See Ananga-Ranga; Erotic Literature; Erotic Art; Kama Sutra; Tantra)

IRIS

The garden iris (Iris germanica) is a perennial named after the goddess of rainbows. Some herbalists believe that the dried rhizome of the purple iris – also knowns as Fleur-de-Lys is the legendary aphrodisiac satyrion. An infusion can be made by steeping two teaspoons of the dried rhizome in a cup of water for about ten minutes. The rhizome should be collected in the third year of growth and ideally dug up after prolonged rainfall. It should then be peeled and dried in the sun.

NEVER use the rhizome of the wild iris (Iris pseudocorus) or Yellow Flag which is poisonous. The illustration on the opposite page is the yellow iris which should NOT be used.

(See Wild Plants for methods and precautions)

IRRUMATIO

A variant of fellatio where the woman remains still and the man moves his penis in her mouth. Gentleness is important as clumsy thrusts may strike the back of the throat and produce gagging (which is unpleasant for the woman) and involuntary biting (which will serve him right).

The so-called 'deep-throat' technique – where the woman is either active or passive – is a spectator sport created by the pornography industry and is to oral lovemaking what riding a monocycle is to bicycling. Professional practioners report that it is also about as comfortable as monocycling once mastered.

(See also FELLATIO)

JADE FLUTE

The traditional Chinese and Japanese term for fellatio where the woman takes the man in her mouth facing him when he is standing, sitting or kneeling. She is then in the best position for fingering the shaft of the penis (as the charming name suggests) and for stimulating the sensitive tip and underside of the glans.
(See also FELLATIO)

JAPAN

'The animal frenzies of the flesh . . . the fury of copulation, as if transported by rage . . .' so wrote Edmond de Goncourt of *shunga*, the erotic prints of Japan. Ironically his visit in the nineteenth century was part of the tide of Western contact and influence which was to result in the end of the most stylish and vigorous tradition of erotic art there has ever been.

However, the fierce art of the eighteenth and nineteenth centuries has survived and gives us a detailed record of the Japanese approach to sex. It could not be more different from Indian lovemaking. The sex depicted in shunga is not equal in any sense. Men have gigantic penises and tidal ejaculations. Orgasms are seismological (the earth always moves) and every encounter has the ferocious formalism of a samurai burying his sword in a victim rather than anything more tender.

In Japan, sexual techniques and pleasures were written about as early as the ninth century AD. By the seventeenth century, when the famous 'Life of a Friend of Voluptuousness' was published, erotic books already contained a large number of toys and gadgets which have always been a feature of Japanese sexuality. Perhaps because of their fondness for bathing and scrupulous personal hygiene, anal techniques of various kinds are more prevalent in Japanese eroticism than in other traditions. The strong taboos associated with such practices in the West may be the result of inferior personal hygiene – which has only comparatively recently achieved levels enjoyed in Japan for centuries – rather than other considerations.
(See also EROTIC ART; PILLOW BOOKS; SEX TOYS)

JASMINE

It takes more than seven million individually picked jasmine blossoms to produce a single kilogram of the absolute from which jasmine oil is made. Jasmine is the intensely feminine note in many of the world's great perfumes and has a long history as an erotic stimulant with a powerful effect on men.
(See also ESSENTIAL OILS; PERFUME AND SCENT; SENSE OF SMELL)

JEWELLERY

Berber dancing girls, in common with social glitterati the world over, wear jewels as an ostentatious display of wealth and an enhancement of their beauty. The cosmetic use of jewellery is well understood and the necklaces, bracelets and other items designed to draw attention to particular features are consciously used as visual aphrodisiacs the world over. Less well-known is the Indian practice of wearing elaborate jewellery and nothing else in lovemaking – which is highly erotic to most men since it emphasizes the nudity of a woman's body while at the same time enhancing its beauty.

Jewellery can also be used as a tactile aphrodisiac. Such devices are usually cosmetic as well and most involve piercing. The most common example are pendant earrings which exerts constant tugging pressure on the earlobe as well as stimulating the nerves of the neck.

Visual stimulus (for those who like it) and pleasurable tugging are the purpose underlying nipple, penile and labial rings, as well as the guiche ring which originated in the South Pacific. This device is inserted in the male perineum and is tugged by his partner to hasten or intensify orgasm.

Genital jewellery can also be designed to intensify pleasure for the partner. In this category are labial bells (which have been likened to copulating with a Christmas tree) and ampallang. In Indonesia some men have these ampallang beads of wood or metal inserted at intervals along their penises. The purpose is to stimulate the clitoris of their partner.

(See also CLOTHES AND FASHION; SEX TOYS)

JUNGLE FOWL

Many sexual practices in the Indian, Japanese and Chinese traditions take their name from the behaviour and appearance of animals. In China the name 'jungle fowl' is

given to a wide range of techniques where another wife (the Chinese were traditionally polygamous) or a female servant contributes or helps. As with other birds (e.g. duck), the mating of jungle fowl often involves a third party whose intentions are not always clear to the casual observer.

The presence of a third party during lovemaking is a potent aphrodisiac for some couples, even if their role is entirely passive. Others derive sexual excitement from being the third party.

(See also PEEPING TOM)

JUNIPER

An evergreen shrub producing fleshy, purple berries which are used for medical purposes, and for flavouring a wide variety of drinks. The national drink of Slovakia, Borowicka, is more strongly-flavoured with juniper than most gins and is probably the most pleasant way of taking a berry with a long-established reputation as an erotic stimulant.

(See also ALCOHOL)

KABBAZAH

An Arab term meaning 'a holder' and used to describe a woman who has the art of grasping with her vagina. Some women are born with this ability while others can learn it with practice. Richard Burton recorded that Arab slave dealers charged vast sums for a woman with this ability. Sheikh Nefzawi, author of The Perfumed Garden, goes so far as to suggest that it is impossible for a man to achieve real sensual pleasure unless his partner applies 'the sucker'.

In some of the most improbable Indian miniature paintings where little or no movement seems possible, or the woman is showing-off by playing a musical instrument while making love, the real point is to demonstrate that she has this ability. She is in charge, and slowly and relentlessly she is milking her partner's penis with her vagina.

The vaginal and pelvic muscles can be developed like any other. It is a much more worthwhile pursuit than purely narcissistic muscle training, not only for the intensification of sexual pleasure but to avoid prolapse in later life.

(See EXERCISE)

KAREZZA

The most commonly-used term for various techniques designed to delay the male orgasm while taking full advantage of the ability which many women possess of enjoying one after the other. Many of the Hindu lovemaking postures – particularly the Tantric bandhas – are specifically intended to minimize male stimulation for this reason, although there are other ritualistic reasons as well. In hermetic Chinese texts it is known as 'Unendurable Pleasure Indefinitely Prolonged'.

There is evidence that taken to extremes these practices are not good for the male prostate, but some skill in the technique is essential if a man is to be a satisfactory lover. There are women who orgasm very quickly but they are rare. Normally the man is fast and a woman slow to respond. Correcting this almost universal mismatch is an example of where Art can definitely improve on Nature.

It may be better for the man to stimulate his partner manually or orally to a point just before or at the beginning of orgasm and then penetrate her. If he has trouble remaining erect she can help or he can keep himself primed.

Tantrists recommend breathing exercises and meditation which amount to much the same thing. By concentrating the mind on anything other than the in-and-out movements of his penis the man can delay until it is time to rejoin the party.

Some people find anaesthetic sprays useful, others find them unaesthetic. There are practised lovers who have a first orgasm, continue foreplay until their erection returns, and take their partner to orgasm with their longer 'second wind'.

Variations of all these techniques are worth experimenting with. Premature ejacu-

lation is a major cause of sexual unhappiness and if all else fails do not hesitate to consult a reputable sex therapist through your doctor. Their success rate is very high.
(See also TANTRA)

KARKATA

This sexual asana translates from Sanskrit as 'the Crab'. As with many Indian lovemaking postures it is less comfortable if the man is not used to the Eastern practice of resting by squatting on the ground with knees raised. A lifetime's practice of resting on haunches means that the joints are used to it and the blood supply to the legs is not affected.

Karkata

KINGFISHER

A Chinese flanquette posture where the man controls friction and sensation for both partners by raising or lowering the woman's leg.

KISS

Kissing is like cooking – everyone can do it after a fashion, the simplest is often the best but also the most abused, and masters of the art can have almost anything they want.

Kissing is the aphrodisiac skill worth perfecting before all others. Both men and women should be skilled, but especially men. Lips and tongue are the basic equipment but they can and should be applied in many different ways, and these should be varied so that the effect is a symphony of sensation and not the oscular equivalent of a vacuum cleaner.

The entire body is the object to be kissed, and if you have not kissed your partner just about everywhere then now is the moment to begin because you are both missing one of the natural wonders of the world. And that is how to approach the body of your lover – as if you were exploring the world. Use your lips as a brush, and your tongue tip in the same way. Suck gently with your lips, suck violently, probe with your tongue. Suit the approach to the place, and vary both. Change pace, pursue an advantage when your lover responds – use your imagination.

Mouth kissing is an explosive aphrodisiac which can be used anywhere. But do not confuse it with the 'mouth pressed hard with deep-tonguing' technique beloved of Hollywood which is *maraichignage* – a different thing needing a different explanation (see that entry). Proceeding straight to deep tonguing can be mutual and spontaneous – so can instant genital penetration with hard thrusting – but usually both should be worked up to.

Try wetting your lips with your tongue and gently taking your lover's upper lip between yours with the lightest suction. Pull away infinitely slowly until you are apart. Then take the lower lip and slowly repeat the pattern. Explore tentatively with your tongue at first, withdraw, invite reciprocation.

Kama Sutra devotes a long chapter to kissing which all lovers should read. In The Perfumed Garden Sheikh Nefzawi also stresses the importance of kissing in lovemaking and is well worth reading. He also mentions saliva exchange which we

Knee Elbow

have in common with other mammals, imaginatively anticipating modern zoology by four hundred years. Japanese pillow books also tell lovers to enjoy the taste of each other's saliva, but Sheikh Nefzawi has the last word: 'a kiss is one of the most potent stimulants that a man or woman can indulge in . . . and is more intoxicating than strong wine'.

(See also BUTTERFLY KISS; MARAICHIGNAGE)

--------- KNEE-ELBOW ---------

A lovemaking position described in the Hindu love manual Ratiradnapradipika: 'If you lift the girl by passing your elbows under her knees and enjoy her as she hangs trembling with her arms garlanding your neck, it is called Janukurpura, the Knee-Elbow'.

Like all fully-supported standing positions it is potentially hazardous for the man and best attempted in water unless he is very strong and sure-footed.

--------- KNOT OF FAME ---------

The Chinese name for this position is *Soaring Butterfly*. It has always been favoured by courtesans because the woman has total control and the man maximum visual and genital stimulation.

--------- LADY'S MANTLE ---------
(*Alchemilla vulgaris*)

A perennial plant which grows in fields and woods. Culpeper drawing on ancient folk tradition said that Lady's Mantle 'inspires lust'. The flowering shoots and leaves should be dried. They can then be boiled in water (two teaspoons of dried plant per cup). Not more than one cup of the liquid a day should be taken – and that

not more than once a week. Simple infusion makes a milder preparation.
(See WILD PLANTS for methods and precautions)

LADY'S WILL

This position is so-called because most movement must be initiated by the woman. Used by Tantrists for orgasm control it is ideal for protracted lovemaking with just sufficient stimulation of the penis to keep it erect while providing constant pressure on the clitoris. Lovers can hold each other, kiss, talk and delay orgasm for a long period while maintaining a gentle rocking movement.

The Ratikallolini says: 'She whose dark eyes are like fallen lotus petals takes your penis and guides it into her vulva, then clings tight to you and shakes her buttocks . . . this is Lady's Will'.

LAMPREYS AND EELS

Henry I of England died from a surfeit of lampreys which are said to stimulate both lust and the production of semen. Interestingly, although they were eaten to increase male potency for many centuries before the invention of microscopy, lampreys resemble spermatazoa.

Eels – possibly because of their phallic shape – are also a favourite aphrodisiac food and were much prized by the Romans for that reason.
(See also EATING AND FOOD; SEAFOOD)

LANGUAGE

All languages have a vocabulary of sexual words which are more potent than those used by doctors and in general conversation. Often these taboo words are a relic of a conquered people whose language – like their religion – is suppressed by the conquerors. This is the case with the 'four-letter' words in English which are part of an Anglo-Saxon inheritance.

Because they are taboo, and because they carry a greater charge than more polite words, many people use this vocabulary to express their feelings during lovemaking.

This can have an aphrodisiac effect both by association and because it reduces inhibition. Both Kama Sutra and the oral Tantric tradition recommend a return to basics in the sounds and language which lovers use together.

In English, four-letter words are used for swearing simply because of their greater potency. This is a quite different use of language and does not debase the word which is usually much older and better than the 'polite' equivalent. Experiment with your heritage.

LAUGHTER

There is an Old Wives's Tale that laughter and bed do not go together. In fact humour can be an important part of foreplay: a useful way of breaking down inhibitions or overcoming any temporary awkwardness. Helpless shared laughter is beneficial and mentally and physically refreshing in much the same way as sex: laughing helps loving, it does not hinder it.

LAVENDER

As nard, which is lavender essence, this was one of the most expensive and popular perfumes of the ancient world. The aroma of lavender was thought to have an aphrodisiac effect but it was also eaten. Lavender can be taken by steeping one teaspoon of the dried flowers in a cup of cold water for ten minutes.
(See WILD PLANTS for methods and precautions; also ESSENTIAL OILS; MASSAGE; PERFUME AND SCENT)

LEAPING WHITE TIGER

The term for various croupade positions in both Japanese and Chinese manuals. Rear entry positions are among the best for strong, uninhibited lovemaking.

LEATHER

The appearance, texture and aroma of leather acts as an aphrodisiac for some people. Like just about everything else it can be a vehicle for fetishistic excess. But that is not a reason to exclude it from your repertoire if you find it stimulating.
(See also CLOTHES AND FASHION)

LEEK

The emperor Nero had leek soup every day to improve his voice for oration and singing but the most common use in Rome was as a mild aphrodisiac. Some experts believe that leek is a cultivated variant of oriental garlic.

The best recipes for leeks are found in the regional cooking of Piedmont and Northern France (especially around Arras) where it is widely grown. Leeks cooked in red wine in the oven are simple to prepare and delicious.
(See PLATE 9)

LEISURE

'Love comes from Leisure' is a shrewd observation made by the writers of love manuals in many different cultures. Pillow books and love manuals themselves have

in the past been produced for those with the time and resources to experiment with sexuality and raise it to an art form. Sex is always one of the first subjects to receive attention in any class or culture with an abundance of leisure. The Maoris of New Zealand who, until the appearance of Europeans, had what amounted to a paradise of plenty all to themselves, are said to have more words for the clitoris than any people on earth.

Most people are not in the position of having to search for ways to fill their leisure time. But proper periods of relaxation are essential for good sex. The modern 'workaholic' is diverting energy to the office which would be better kept in the bedroom.

LIQUORICE

Meaning 'sweet root' in Greek, liquorice was used extensively in medicine through-out the ancient world. In small quantities liquorice was believed to have an aphro-disiac effect and in Chaucer's day was added to beer for that purpose.
(See PLATE 4)

LINEN

Scented bed linen was once a popular aphrodisiac. Louis XIV used many different formulas including ingredients such as clove and nutmeg, as well as the more traditional aromas of jasmine and rose.

Sachets for perfuming linen drawers and pillows are becoming popular again, but it is better to experiment with aromas which you respond to rather than the multifloral concoctions of manufacturers. Remember that too much scent is a power-ful anaphrodisiac.
(See also CASSOLETTE; ESSENTIAL OILS; PERFUME AND SCENT; POMANDERS; SENSE OF SMELL)

LIVER

According to the Roman poet Horace, liver was widely believed to have aphrodisiac properties.
(See also APHRODISIACS)

LOBSTER

The finest of all shellfish and a popular feature in erotic cuisine. The texture, taste, colour and smell of freshly-cooked lobster are without equal. Eating lobster should be a tactile experience: use your fingers and do it yourself or you will be missing half of the fun. The pre-bed meal in the film Tom Jones gives a good idea of the way lovers can derive the maximum pleasure from lobster as a piece of erotic theatre. Lobster is expensive but worth every penny.
(See also EATING AND FOOD; SEAFOOD)

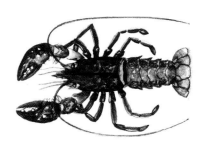

LOVAGE

A pleasant herb with mild deodorizing properties. In Moravia and Bohemia it was mixed with fenugreek as a love charm.
(See FENUGREEK)

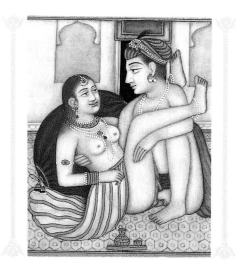

Love God's Love

LOVE BITES

Not bites at all but the reddening or bruising of sensitive skin by sucking it between pursed lips and teeth. Some people find these marks exciting as visible evidence of passion. If passion was not involved of course the whole point is lost since they are not an end in themselves but a sign so that lovers can remember what has been. Adolescent girls often collect them in much the same way that boys collect stamps – often just as innocently.

Real biting and marking with the teeth is dealt with at some length in Kama Sutra, one of the few features of the work which is not readily accessible to our culture. Biting one another in the throes of passion (preferably nowhere sensitive) is easily understood. But Kama Sutra's elaborate language of markings and bites is as indecipherable and incomprehensible as cuneiform.
(See also INDIA; KAMA SUTRA)

LOVE GOD'S LOVE

In this posture the woman's legs are hooked over her lover's arms, her back supported by cushions. His hand movement is restricted but she can co-ordinate the pace by touching her clitoris or by holding him in the *Florentine* position.
(See also *FLORENTINE*)

LUTE

A Hindu deep penetration position. In China this posture is called *Monkey's Attack*.

MACE

This culinary – long regarded as aphrodisiac – spice also yields an essential oil (Myristica fragrans) which is used in perfumery. Mace has a warm, 'male' note: the essential oil can be added to massage oil.
(See also ESSENTIAL OILS; MASSAGE)

MALLOW or MARSH MALLOW

(*Althaea officinalis*)

A perennial plant found growing near the sea and close to marshy ground. Mallow was believed to have an aphrodisiac effect on women according to Pliny the Elder.

The ancient recipe was to steep the mallow in goat's milk. Best taken as an infusion of no more than one teaspoon of dried leaves per cup.
(See WILD PLANTS for methods and precautions)

Lute

MANDARIN DUCKS

A well-known sexual posture in both Chinese and Japanese erotology. For a full description see the Indian 'Cobra' position.

In the West this method of lovemaking is sometimes called 'spoon fashion' because the woman is entered from the rear and the couple fit together like spoons.

Provided she is well-lubricated it is a good posture if the man has been ill or does not have a hard erection for some reason. Perhaps that is why the fifteenth-century Zen poet Ikkyu used it with his lover the blind servant girl Mori:

'Deep in the boudoir, how much poetry.
A song before the wind-blow flowers, the purity of this fragrant banquet.
Making love on the bed, a feeling of the river and the sea.
To spend the rest of our lives like mandarin ducks, at ease on the water.'

MANDRAKE

The plant *Mandragora officinarum* was used in ancient medicine as a sleeping draught. Shakespeare often mentions it and has Cleopatra say:

'Give me to drink mandragora
That I might sleep out the great gap of time
My Anthony is away.'

The mandrake root, which often grows in strange and suggestive shapes, has always been a favourite prop of charlatans and quacks. Perhaps for this reason supposed

aphrodisiac qualities have been added to its known purgative effects.
MANDRAKE SHOULD NOT BE EATEN.
(See also PHILTRES AND POTIONS)

MARAICHIGNAGE

A deep tonguing kiss said to take its name from the inhabitants of the Pays de Mont in the Vendée (Brittany) who are known as The Maraichins. Each partner explores the other's mouth in a tongue battle simulating genital penetration.

Maraichignage, which is also known as French kissing, has often been used with heavy petting as a substitute for genital sex. Many people enjoy the stimulation of tongue and mouth and saliva exchange involved, and continue maraichignage during lovemaking.

Because it is both suggestive and permissable, Hollywood and television have rather over-exposed what is a useful technique but not the beginning and the end of kissing.
(See also KISSING)

MARE

A Sanskrit manual describes this technique: 'When, straightening her legs, she grips and milks your penis with her vagina – as a mare holds a stallion – it is Vadavaka, the Mare, which is not learned without practice'. The Chinese call this 'splitting the Cicada.'

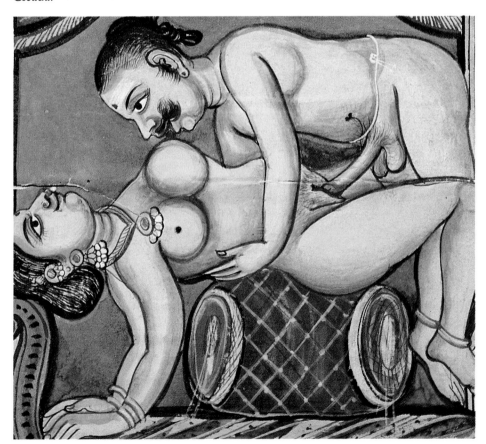

MARIGOLD

(See BRIDE CAKES AND WEDDING FOOD)

MASKS AND BLINDFOLDS

Really quite different things with entirely different erotic possibilities, although they are often put together.

Masks were once the fashion, at a time when assignation and discreet infidelity were an accepted way of life for the leisured classes. Ladies and their paramours could flirt openly while maintaining an illusion of anonymity among their peers; more importantly they could visit each other's houses unrecognized. They could also, if they wished, make love masked which many found exciting – and still do.

In a mask you can be other than you are and the person you are with can be anyone you choose. If the mask is elaborate and not simply a dark shape, the wearer takes on the 'personality' of the mask. Masks are worn in some religious rituals for the same reason. Masks are not solely the prerogative of sado-masochists and can be used for lighthearted sexual games as they have been at Carnival in Venice and elsewhere for many centuries.

Blindfolds work in a quite different way. They cause disorientation in the wearer and feelings of vulnerability. They also intensify the remaining senses and increase the possibility of surprise. All these are reasons why they are used in interrogation techniques of course, but there are also less sinister erotic applications which some people find exciting. A strong, dominant male becomes vulnerable and passive when blindfolded, which can be an interesting role reversal for both partners. In riding him, which is the logical conclusion, the temporary reversal is completed.

Many people – especially if games or theatre are not part of their personality – may find masks and blindfolds absurd or kinky, or both. But this book is a menu, and the more comprehensive a menu is the less probable it is that someone will like every dish.

MASSAGE

This book is about aphrodisiacs, so we are not concerned with the highly-skilled and vigorous business of therapeutic massage, nor with Swedish massage or anything involving hand chopping or skeletal manipulation. Leave all that to the professionals – at least your experiments will be unsatisfactory, at worst they could be harmful.

Lovers can and should experiment with light massage. The three basic actions are Effleurage, Petrissage and Finger Point.

Effleurage is stroking with the whole hand, gently and firmly. Not too lightly – that stimulates only the hairs and skin surface, is akin to tickling and a different technique altogether (see PATTES D'ARAIGNÉE).

Petrissage is kneading – as you would bread dough – with the whole hand. The pressure is firm but not painful.

Finger Point is for stimulating particular trigger points, either with small circular movements of the pad of one or more fingers, or by using the thumb to massage in the way that comes naturally to thumbs.

There are many other techniques but these are the basics. A good way of learning

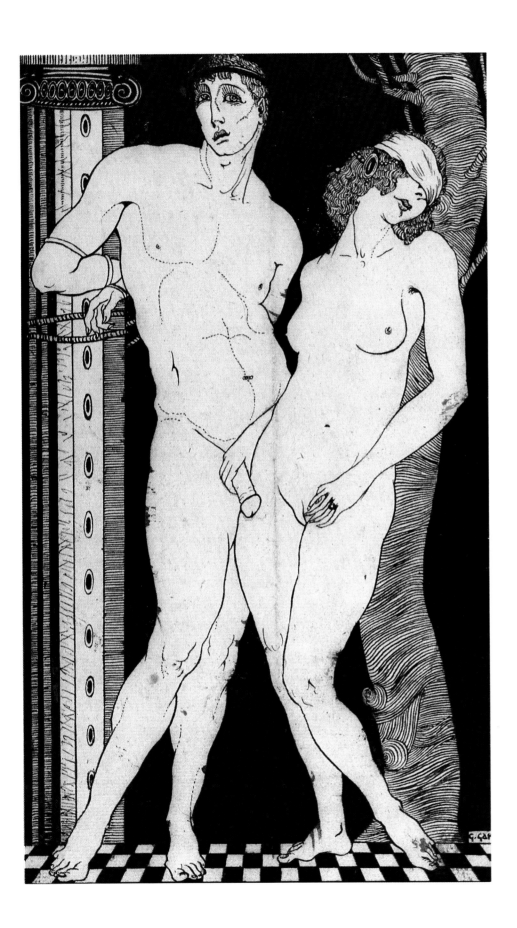

to massage is to watch a professional massaging you – but as with sexual techniques, most people prefer to develop their skills by private experiment.

Oil is not mandatory but it adds another tactile sensation as well as the possibility of perfume. The entry on ESSENTIAL OILS lists those with special erotic associations. Only use a few drops of essential oil to perfume a non-sticky base oil such as grapeseed, almond, or hazelnut – the last two are reputed aphrodisiacs in their own right. The stimulating essential oils are not only inhaled, they soak into the skin. The range of essential oils generally available is enormous. Many culinary herbs and spices are available as essential oils (e.g. Anis, Basil, Bay, Black Pepper, Cardamom, Cinnamon, Coriander, Cumin, Fennel, Ginger, Mace, Marjoram, Nutmeg, Rosemary and Vanilla) and it is fun to experiment with those you like and even to blend them. See the entry on ESSENTIAL OILS for the proportions and method. Do not use too much oil in massage and do not get oil with essential oil added near mucous membrane (vulva or anus) in any quantity. For a vivid account of what astringent substances in the bottom feel like see David Niven's autobiography 'The Moon's a Balloon'.

Aphrodisiac massage is intended to end with sex – genital, oral or manual, or a combination of all three. Therefore a warm room and a surface which you can spill oil on happily is important. If you do not like the idea of oil on the sheets or making love on a large bathtowel – forget the oil. A sheet specifically for massage is the best answer. It is a shame to consign massage to the bathroom unless yours is particularly sumptuous. Experiment with foot massage first of all.

Unless you massage the calf you will not need petrissage which is better for parts such as buttocks and thighs. Feet are very sensitive (see FOOT) and there are supposed erotic triggers just above the heel and below the ankle bone on both sides. Between the toes is very important, as is a line running along the middle of the underside between heel and ball. If you are not using oil (or perhaps even if you are) try sucking toes individually. Always keep massage balanced: both feet, both arms, both sides of the body. And to keep everything balanced, your partner should massage your feet after you have finished. Foot massage is relaxing, sensual and a good way to begin.

On a different occasion (massage is tiring on the hands) explore the rest of your partner's body and use petrissage, particularly on large muscles. The purpose of aphrodisiac massage is to find individual erotic triggers and to relax and stimulate your partner's body at the same time. Try to keep communication tactile and visual unless something is painful or irritating. Too much talking is an anaphrodisiac for both parties.

Men's bodies tend to be more predictable, but women often have very sensitive, non-genital trigger points (see also BREASTS AND NIPPLES). If you are not finding some unexpected ones you are not looking hard enough or being sufficiently imaginative in varying pressure and technique.

Some good places to concentrate your search in either sex correspond to some of the acupuncture points and meridians. For example the 'milk line' that runs from the middle finger up the centre of the palm and the inside of the arm and across to the nipple.

The central lower back above the buttocks, along the spine and immediately either side is another good area for sexual trigger points. Also a straight line from above the pubic hair to the navel, and the whole of the perineum – the area between vulva and anus or scrotum and anus.

Constantly vary technique and pressure of hand or fingers, and use lips or erect penis as an alternative if it seems appropriate. A harem tehnique which has been commercialized in the Far East is 'total body massage'. Both partners are anointed with a bland oil and the woman uses the whole of her body to massage the man. Alternatively you can take turns in exciting and exploring each other, taking full advantage of your new-found lubricity!
(See also BREASTS AND NIPPLES; ESSENTIAL OILS; FOOT; PATTES D'ARAIGNÉE)

MASTURBATION

Statistics indicate that 85 per cent of women and 95 per cent of men masturbate themselves. Unfortunately not all of them do so in an untroubled, guiltless way because of the prejudices and Old Wives Tales which are associated with mastur-

bation. There are psychological disorders in which compulsive masturbation is a component (NOT a cause) but self-masturbation is normal healthy behaviour. It is normal for it to occur within a full and satisfactory sex life with a partner – it is a different thing, with a different nuance of sensation and it does not necessarily imply that the partner is failing in some way. Masturbation is not as good or fulfilling as sex with a partner, it can never be. But there is nothing wrong with it as even some otherwise sexually sophisticated people persist in believing.

In the absence of a partner masturbation is essential. If you are middle-aged and alone it is a good idea to masturbate in order to keep your body alive to sex and your hormones in full production. You will look better, feel better and not have any problems resuming a sexually active life if a partner comes along.

Guilt is probably the most effective anaphrodisiac of them all, which is why the more repressed and repressive Victorian teachers combined it with cold baths and left us with a legacy of ignorance and misery. The main reason for including masturbation in a book on aphrodisiacs is its importance in lovemaking.

Masturbation is the only way of learning about our own sexual responses, which is why sex therapists use it when women have orgasm problems. You can hardly expect someone else to give you an orgasm if you cannot do it yourself and do not fully understand your own responses. Masturbation is also a way of learning about your partner: doing it to yourself for your partner as a piece of erotic drama is not only a powerful visual aphrodisiac (next time together!) it is also instructive.

Learning how someone masturbates is important because all good lovers do it for each other as a regular part of lovemaking. In women it is chiefly to bring them closer to orgasm (though it need not be); in men it is used in foreplay to achieve and maintain erection, and as an important end in itself. Women who feel let down and unloved if a man does not always erect spontaneously without being masturbated are displaying sad ignorance of male physiology. Put that in the Victorian box room together with the other junk like 'women don't enjoy sex', 'washing is unmanly'.

Masturbation is an additional pleasure you can give your male partner and an essential skill for a woman. Do it for a change, for a second or third orgasm in protracted lovemaking, or simply when he is tired and you want to please him. It is not simply economics or fear of disease which have kept masturbation among the most important skills a prostitute has in her armoury. At some periods, notably in Paris and Venice, there were professionals who only pleased men in that way.

The best way to discover how your lover likes to be masturbated is to ask him to show you. He is not as sensitive as you are but clumsiness with his glans or the tight skin under the foreskin if he is uncircumcized is painful and very anaphrodisiac!

A technique he may not know himself is to masturbate him by moving the loose skin on the shaft of the penis up and down. When he is close to orgasm but before contractions begin, pull the skin back from the glans tightly (but not too tightly) and wait. Do not move at all, even when he begins to ejaculate – only after his ejaculation is nearly over, move down again to the loose skin to complete matters with a few more strokes. The effect – if you get it right – will tell you why masturbation is a skill to be perfected.

In masturbating her do not concentrate only on the clitoris. Ask her to show you how she does it herself. Finally, it must be said that the tongue is a better instrument for masturbating a woman than a finger.
(See GAMAHUCHE)

MIMICRY

It is a characteristic of human sexual and other behaviour that we often do to others what we would like them to do to us. Sensitive lovers are aware of this and use it to improve their lovemaking. Mimicry is a concept which can be helpful rather than a precise technique. But if she spends a good deal of time nibbling your earlobes when you have never expressed any particular desire for it, it may be worth reciprocating.

MINT

This widely-used culinary herb has some reputation as an aphrodisiac, especially for men. Shakespeare classes it with lavender, savory and marjoram as being useful as a stimulant for 'men of middle-age' in 'The Winter's Tale' – one of his last plays and written when he may have been interested in such matters.

MIRRORS

Simple and very effective aphrodisiacs which have always been used to good effect in the best bordellos. Many sexual postures offer good tactile stimulus but low visual excitement. For example a woman may find rear-entry positions unsatisfactory for that reason. A carefully placed mirror is the solution. Looking in a mirror also enables both lovers to see all the action rather than half of it, which is important sometimes. Our own bodies can be visually exciting. To glimpse ourselves making love also affirms and underlines the fact of our lovemaking and heightens the eroticism.
(See also BORDELLOS)

MISSIONARY POSITION (See ADAM AND EVE)

MISTLETOE
(Viscum album)

The English practice of 'kissing under the mistletoe' obviously has its origins in pagan fertility rituals. The semen-like berries and the leaves have been used in folk medicine and by modern herbalists but dosage is extremely critical. **MISTLETOE SHOULD NOT BE EATEN.**

MONKEY

In this Hindu posture the position of the legs should be varied to achieve different effects: his between hers, hers together, or flanquette.
(See also FLANQUETTE)

MOUNTAIN FACING TREE

A Taoist lovemaking posture where the woman rides the man. He lies on his back and she faces away from him stimulating her own clitoris as she rises and falls on him.

MUGWORT
(Artemisia vulgaris)

Related to wormwood (artemisia absinthium) with reputed aphrodisiac effects. The chopped, flowering herb sprinkled over fat pork, duck or goose is a marvellous

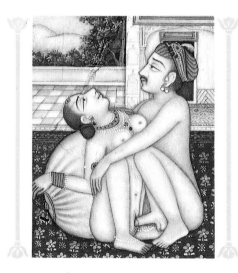

Monkey

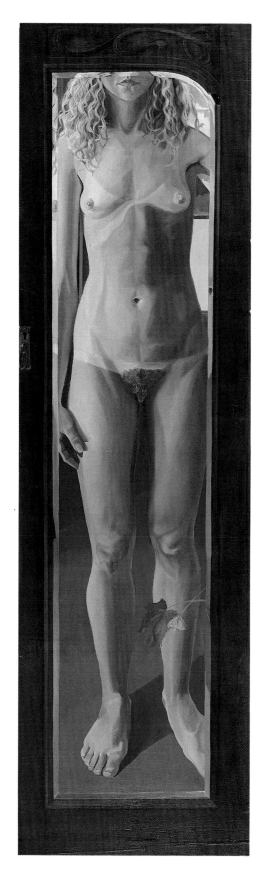

condiment. It can also be used as a herb in white sauces with fish, especially eel. Mugwort should not be taken in high concentration or over long periods. (See WILD PLANTS for methods and precautions)

MULBERRY

The luscious and delicately flavoured black mulberry (white mulberry is delicious only to silkworms) is an age-old aphrodisiac. In plant mythology it is associated with the tragic lovers Pyramus and Thisbe, the red stains below a mulberry tree symbolizing the blood from their broken hearts.

Pomegranate

Mulberry

PLATE 10

MUSHROOM

Perhaps because of their often phallic appearance and suggestive male odour, mushrooms were regarded as a sexual stimulant by many Arab physicians.

If you have never fried button mushrooms lightly in a little oil, adding chopped garlic and a dash of sherry or sweet wine at the last moment – include the dish in your list of aphrodisiac hors d'oeuvres.

MUSIC

Literature, and real life, is full of musical seducers: the demonic virtuoso violinist, the student playing Chopin polonaises to his girlfriend and the rock star in a stadium

107

are notoriously successful sexually because of the aphrodisiac effect of music. As individuals they may be unremarkable, but they are the medium for an infinitely powerful art – they share in its glamour and become associated with it in the mind of the listener who is vulnerable to the opportunistic seducer while under its influence.

Music's power to excite and 'carry away' is not fully understood and this is not the place to analyze the genius of the great composers or the magic of the soloist. Some noticeably 'erotic' music has an insistent heartbeat rhythm (e.g. Ravel's Bolero) other pieces use crescendo in a way which parallels sexual excitement and release, but it is obviously more complicated than that.

All that is important is to remember that music is a potent mood setter and aphrodisiac, and can be used in that way.

(See also DANCE; PERFORMING ARTS)

MUSK

Real musk is derived from a gland near the genitals of the musk-deer. As it is very expensive, perfumes often imitate it with blends of the vegetable essential oils ambrette and angelica which cannot replicate the pheromones which are the real point of musk (see SENSE OF SMELL).

The original purpose of musk is to carry sexual signals to other musk-deer. When combined with different aromas by perfumers it has the ability to 'carry' those to human noses. Some women value musk on its own as a sexual allure for their own species. It is not a new idea – courtesans used to carry small bladders of it about their person in order to burst them at suitably erotic moments.

The absence of unpleasant incidents involving women who use the substance as a perfume and male musk-deer can only be explained by the relative scarcity of the animal.

(See also ESSENTIAL OILS; PERFUMERY AND SCENT)

MUSSELS

A delicious and widely-available shellfish with a long reputation as an aphrodisiac. The erotic association may derive from the impudent internal organs of this bivalve which often surprise the unwary eater. The Italians call the mussel cozzo which means 'cock'.

(See also EATING AND FOOD; SEAFOOD)

MUSTARD

A Roman importation into Northern Europe, mustard is a valuable spice and an essential ingredient in many sauces and dishes. In the Arab world it has long been prized as a sexual stimulant.

MYSTIC

In this position the woman sits on the curled leg of her lover and raises her own. Not quite as difficult as it looks, but best attempted on a soft bed with plenty of cushions and pillows.

Mystic

NAGARA

A partly-pressed asana giving deep penetration. If this is the final position they will adopt in their lovemaking she may need to stimulate her own clitoris to bring her to orgasm.

NARD (See Lavender)

NAVEL

A highly erogenous and sadly neglected feature of our bodies. Tongue and finger stimulation of the navel can be exciting for both men and women.

By holding one of his lover's feet the man is able to vary the sensation of each thrust. As with all deep penetration positions the man should take care not to bruise an ovary with clumsy lunging.

NETTLE
(*Urtica dioica and Urtica urens*)

The very young shoots of nettles which contain vitamin C can be added to salads or cooked like spinach. The juice expressed from freshly-picked nettles (1 large spoonful, 3 times a day) has been used as a sexual stimulant and as a hair tonic.
(See WILD PLANTS for methods and precautions)

NIMITTA

A standing variant of *soixante-neuf*: for the woman an orgasm achieved in this position can be very intense. The posture should only be attempted with the partial support of a bed (at first) and plenty of pillows or cushions. This is not an asana but a Tantric bandha, or knot – a way of channeling the energy released by sex from one partner to the other. The woman in the carving of the *nimitta* position is turning to suck her lover – a variation best left to the double-jointed.
(See also TANTRA)

NUTMEG

The Chinese are particularly fond of this spice which is believed to have an aphrodisiac effect. The seeds are harvested from the same evergreen tree which provides the spice mace. Nutmeg is very useful in cooking but should only be used in small quantities as in large doses it may be poisonous. Various disorders have been attributed to the enormous Victorian appetite for this spice.

Nimitta

OCEANIC

Frontal sexual positions: where the man squats or kneels between the woman's legs. In Polynesia and Micronesia this is the most commonly used method (which is why it has been called 'oceanic') but it is also popular among many of the peoples of Asia, Africa and South America.

ONIONS

Botanically this aromatic vegetable belongs to the lily family and is thought to have originated in centra Asia. The Chaldeans, Egyptians, Greeks and Romans all revered the onion which has always been regarded as an aphrodisiac. There are many different varieties of onion which can be used in different ways. One specifically aphrodisiac recipe popular in Arab countries is to mix cooked, chopped onion with scrambled egg.

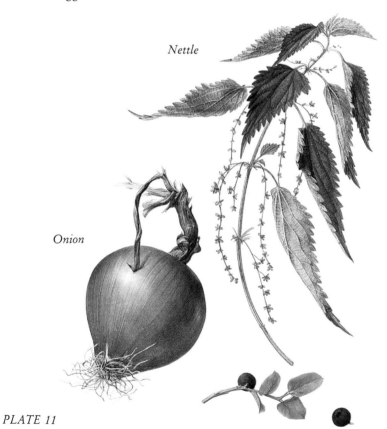

Nettle

Onion

PLATE 11

As with garlic and the other strong aromatics which often feature in aphrodisiac cooking, it is important for you both to have some.
(See also EROTIC CUISINE)

OPENING FLOWER

In this lovemaking position it is essential for the woman to be raised on high cushions. Alternatively the side of the bed can be used.

OREGANO

A useful culinary herb which sometimes features in aphrodisiac recipes, especially those of Greece and the Levant.

OYSTER

There is an old joke that a man was prescribed two dozen oysters as an aphrodisiac by an authority on sexual matters. The next day he complained that only the first twenty-three had worked.

The Romans, with their extraordinary appetite for both food and sex, were the first to regard oysters as an aphrodisiac. The poet Ausonius wrote a long poem about the many different types to be found from Colchester to Bordeaux, and from Marseilles to Greece. Juvenal said that 'shameless and lascivious women' used oysters as an aphrodisiac: 'Take head or tail, to her 'tis much the same, who at midnight on plump oysters sups.'

Eating oysters is a sensuous experience: appearance, smell, sensation in the mouth and taste are all equally important. The best way to have oysters is raw, just as they are. Never drink spirits before, during or after eating them as the effect is very unpleasant.

Oysters are rich in zinc, which is an important mineral for a good sex life, but their real aphrodisiac value is sensual. Casanova successfully seduced two nuns with oysters and champagne.

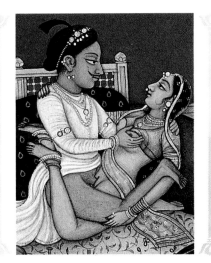

Pallava

—————————— PAIRING SWALLOWS ——————————

A Japanese sexual posture: manual stimulation of the clitoris is necessary unless the man leans forward into a higher position (see illustration on following page).

—————————— *PALLAVA* ——————————

In this posture – which means 'bud' – the lovers 'sit' into each other. This is one of the many orgasm-delaying positions used in Tantra.
(See TANTRA)

—————————— PAPRIKA ——————————

A mild, red spice made from sweet pepper (Capsicum annum) and used for colouring and flavouring in Hungarian cookery. Many paprika recipes are said to be aphrodisiac.
(See also PEPPER)

—————————— *PARAVARTITA* ——————————

A stylized version of a Tantric bandha: definitely only to be attempted by adepts.

Paravartita

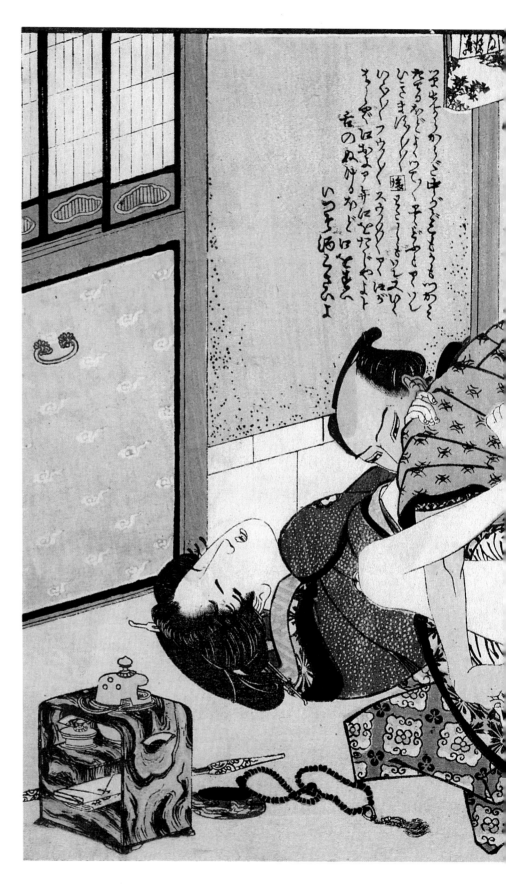

Pairing Swallows

PARSLEY

This well-known herb is a very important source of vitamin C when fresh and is widely used in sauces and as a garnish. Parsley has an extraordinary variety of magical and mythological associations. It has been regarded as an aphrodisiac and as an essential ingredient in the magic which enabled witches to fly. The phallic witch's broom which was rubbed with parsley may in fact be another echo of ancient fertility ritual which seems to be the real origin of parsley's supposed powers.

(See PLATE 3)

PARTRIDGE

A favourite ingredient in erotic cuisine accompanied by strongly spiced sauces.
(See EROTIC CUISINE; GAME)

PATTES D'ARAIGNÉE

To see the startling effect which this erotic massage technique can have once perfected, try a simple experiment. Stand in front of a mirror and pass a finger tip along the edge of your upper lip as lightly as you can – touching but not touching (an experiment which also indicates what kissing can be).

Pattes d'araignée means 'spiders' feet' and the idea is to brush your finger tips over your lover's skin surface so lightly that the microscopic hairs are stimulated as much as the skin surface itself. This is another courtesan's skill which can be learned with practice and has an electrifying effect on men and women. The technique is to use all the finger tips of an open hand (both hands if you are dextrous) and to make long strokes across your lover's body. Concentrate on the less obvious erogenous areas: the side of the rib cage, buttocks, inner thighs, inner arm. As the massage proceeds nipples and pubic hair should be included.

The ideal transition from Pattes d'araignée to lovemaking is via gamahuche or fellatio. But that is a matter of taste.

(See also MASSAGE; SKIN)

PEACH

Perhaps the most sensuous of all fruits: an abundance of intensely flavoured juice contained within a downy cleavage. Peaches also make all the right colour signals as a visual aphrodisiac: blushing pinks and clearly-defined red areas (once the stone is removed). The great beauty Madame Ricarnier, when she was close to death and without appetite, was given the will to live again by being fed peaches and cream,

The peach, which is exceptionally rich in vitamins A and C, originated in China where it was cultivated as early as 2000 BC. It came into Europe, together with all its erotic associations, via Persia and is now grown throughout the world.

(See also EATING AND FOOD)

PEAR

The shape of pears, with their echoes of female anatomy, have always fascinated artists. Some varieties also have a blush which is an erotic signal the human male is

Pearl Necklace

conditioned to respond to. Pears are rich in vitamins A, B and C as well as containing a useful amount of iodine.

The unique texture of the flesh, and its shape, make the pear a regular feature in erotic cuisine.

(See EROTIC CUISINE)

PEARL

The seminal pearl born – like Aphrodite herself – in the ocean has many erotic associations. The subtlety and lustrous glow of pearls have made them an essential feature of great jewellery and costume at different times. At their first great banquet together (Anthony's place among history's great eaters is even more secure than his reputation as a lover) Cleopatra dissolved a priceless pearl in lemon juice and raised her glass to Mark Anthony. Whether this was a symbolic gesture (her skill in fellatio was legendary) or pure extravagance is not recorded.

PEARL NECKLACE

The descriptive popular term for a sex game which the texbooks call 'intra mammary intercourse'. The man's penis, suitably lubricated, is moved between his lover's breasts (the 'pearl necklace' refers of course to his ejaculate). It offers interesting anthropological and psychological insights and is a service which the more ample courtesans have always offered. *Pearl Necklace* need not be concerned only with the man's pleasure: many women can achieve orgasm by stimulation of their breasts and nipples alone, although the technique can of course be combined with manual stimulation of her sex.

PEEPING TOM

Tradition has been rather unkind to the only man in Coventry who looked when Lady Godiva rode naked through the town. Voyeurism – where watching takes the place of doing – is of course an illness, but if anyone had a problem in Coventry it was Lady Godiva.

Setting out to spy on people who are naked or making love (even if you are a policeman or a priest) is despicable of course. But to deny that the occasional accidental glimpses of such things which life provides us with are both exciting and interesting is hypocrisy. Observation can also be instructive, and it is no accident that societies which have had a less repressed attitude towards these things have produced the best instructive erotic literature.

PEPPER

This includes all the fruits of the genus *Capsicum* which takes its name from the Greek word for 'bite'. There are two main spices: the sweet peppers (Capsicum annum) which are eaten as vegetables; and the hot, spicy peppers (Capsicum frutescens) which are eaten only as an appetizer or used to season other food.

Some of the sweet peppers, notably those which are red, have been regarded as aphrodisiac food. All of the hot peppers have. The strength and flavour vary enormously depending on the type and which part is eaten – whole fresh fruit;

whole dried fruit; or the seed or peppercorn, which can be black (with skin), white (skin removed) or green (immature). The common fiery substance is the alkaloid capsaicin.

Pepper is so universally regarded as an aphrodisiac that an entire book could be devoted to recipes. One to try is steak au poivre, using the tangy green peppercorns and not the black which are best for grinding. Fry the steak using butter. At the last moment before serving add a dash of brandy (this can be flamed if you like theatre) a sprinkling of crushed green peppercorns and a little cream.
(See also EATING AND FOOD; EROTIC CUISINE)

Erotic performances designed to have an aphrodisiac effect on the spectator have been a feature of many cultures. At its most basic and (most people find) least stimulating this consists of watching couples copulate. This is not sex except in the most basic sense and was probably as boring when staged for various European Courts or in the bazaars of North Africa as it now is in Amsterdam's red light district. Blue movies are usually boring for similar reasons – all too often no art or imagination is involved and one feels desperately sorry for the participants.

More interesting is erotic dancing. Both men and women have always found this art stimulating. It includes forms as diverse as striptease, belly dancing, flamenco and the can-can. In ancient India dance was often highly erotic: its positions echoing those of lovemaking and also called asanas. In addition to its visual impact, erotic dancing involves rhythm and music, both of which can also be aphrodisiac.

The theatre has an ancient erotic tradition. Pantomime in ancient Greece and Rome was far removed from the innocent entertainment which fills British theatres in the festive season. Both have people dressed in the clothes of the opposite sex, but the ancient version was more likely to feature a giant phallus than a beanstalk, and the pantomime horse tended to mount the leading lady if Martial is to be believed.

The intellectual comedies of Aristophanes and his contemporaries also had sex as a dominant theme. Every possibility and perversion was dealt with in a bawdy and satirical way. In Rome, 'theatre and 'brothel' were almost interchangeable and when the plays were over audience participation often began.

Modern sex comedy seems tame compared with the razor wit and frank eroticism of theatre in the ancient world. And contemporary 'revue' is a pale and often shabby copy of the aphrodisiac entertainment once available in Alexandria or Rome.

Of all the performing arts specifically erotic in intention, dance is by far the most varied and interesting. It is also, when well done, the most aphrodisiac.

PERFUME AND SCENT

The aphrodisiac most commonly used in our society is perfume – most of us use it in one form or another as an excitant and erotic advertisement. There are many similarities between the way perfume is sold to us by the advertising industry and the way we use perfume to 'sell' ourselves: the common weapons are association, imitation and of course sex.

Perfume is a large and very profitable industry: it is no accident that the perfume department is the first enticement to confront prospective customers when they enter most large stores. But all this is alright. Many of the ingredients in good perfume are extremely expensive and magic is more potent when you have to pay dearly for it. Most important of all is the fact that no confidence trick is involved – perfume can work with our own bodies as an aphrodisiac.

A surprisingly large part of our brain is concerned with the olfactory sense (see SENSE OF SMELL). Perfumers mix different aromas to stimulate and please the sense of smell just as a cocktail waiter will combine different elements to appeal to our sense of taste. But the resultant intoxication is not the initial stimulation followed by depression which tends to be the action of alcohol. The intoxication which perfume can produce is part psychological, part sensual – and it continues while the scent remains.

The perfumer's art is extremely subtle and infinitely more skilled than the mixing of cocktails. The perfumer must start with a good sense of smell and then train it to distinguish between the myriad of different aromas which can be combined to create a new perfume. These aromas are derived from many different animal and vegetable sources (see ESSENTIAL OILS) and the list is almost limitless.

All this has only established the palette. The real skill comes in combining different elements, in different proportions, in order to create a complex aroma that is exciting, evocative, attractive and – therefore – aphrodisiac. Perfumery is both an art and a science. It involves time, study, experimentation, creativity, luck and not a little magic.

In choosing a perfume for yourself do not take the activities of the advertising industry into account. They have told you that a new perfume is available – a new sensation that you can try. That is all they can do. You will never smell precisely like the girl (or man) in the advertisement – nor would you want to. You have your own scent which is unique to you (see CASSOLETTE) to which you may or may not add the new perfume. Do not be shy about trying new perfumes from the testers, there is no obligation to buy. Treat perfume as another art: watch to see what is new.

A perfume may or may not contain those aromas which are traditionally said to be aphrodisiac (e.g. jasmine) but you cannot be sure if it is going to work as an aphrodisiac for you until you try it on your skin. Very rarely – great care is taken to avoid it – a new perfume may react with something in your body chemistry and smell bad. Much more commonly it simply will not appeal to you: despite all the advertising it does not seem to fit you. Always take heed of your instincts because they are infallible.

What you are doing unconsciously is comparing the new perfume with your own combined body scent or cassolette. If you have no strong feelings one way or the other, again you should reject the perfume. Your reaction may take a little time but it should be definite and positive. Not only should the perfume combine well with your own scent, it should – albeit unconsciously – evoke associations and memories which please and excite. If a new perfume is not very pleasureable, if it does not work on your imagination and make you daydream – then it is not for you.

It may take you a long time to find the right perfume – it should unless you are very lucky. A perfect match with your own scent and personal aroma aesthetics (e.g. a love of the East) and memory (e.g. first kiss in a rose garden) is rare and once found should not be abandoned lightly. Some women may have two favourite perfumes, perhaps for different occasions and therefore associated with different clothes (which retain perfume). Three perfumes is also feasible but about as rare as three simultaneous loves. Having many perfumes is rather like promiscuous sex.

If a perfume is right it affirms and enhances you. When you look in the mirror and you are pleased with your appearance your confidence and attractiveness increase. If you are pleased with your perfume, confidence and attractiveness are boosted in much the same way. Looking and feeling good have a lot to do with sexual attractiveness. At this point perfume goes into overdrive, because it works with the real aphrodisiac which is your cassolette. Courtesans used to dab a little of their own sexual secretion behind their ears together with perfume. They knew by experience that this enhanced their sexual attractiveness and would have assumed it had something to do with smell. It does. We produce hormonal substances called pheromones to attract partners. Feeling 'attractive' stimulates their production. As we become sexually excited we produce even more and stronger pheromones.

A woman whose perfume combines well with her own pheromones, and consequently is helping to fill the air around her with them, is as well-equipped with aphrodisiacs as it is possible to be.

(See SENSE OF SMELL)

PERFUMED GARDEN

Of all the Arab sex manuals, The Perfumed Garden, written for the Grand Vizier of Tunis by Sheikh Nefzawi in the early sixteenth century, is the most famous. Its notoriety is due in part to Sir Richard Burton's excellent translation which was published in 1886 and also to the burning of his revised and enlarged manuscript by Lady Burton after his death.

The Perfumed Garden was not written with the same pious intention as the Hindu love manuals. Together with sound sexual advice – the importance of foreplay, of kissing – are anecdotes and stories designed to amuse and titillate. Sheikh Nefzawi's urbane work belongs with the bawdy tales of Boccaccio or novels like John Cleland's Fanny Hill rather than with Kama Sutra and Ananga-Ranga. Nevertheless the author had evidently drunk deeply from life's cup and the sexual information is for the most part sound, first-hand material and no less valuable for being larded with humour.

PESTLE

A technique described splendidly in one of the later Indian manuals: 'Stretched wide in the middle of the bed, she lies joined to you in lovemaking, her breathless cries mounting as you polish the jewel of her clitoris: this is mausala, the Pestle'.

PHALLUS

The magic-wand properties of the penis have resulted in its (almost) universal veneration in different parts of the world at different times. The awesome lingam of Shiva – often represented with the yoni of his consort – and the penis emblems which are an important feature of Shinto shrines, are contemporary examples.

In ancient Greece and Rome many thousands of phalluses were erected (literally) to Dionysus, Priapus and other fertility gods. The erect penis was more than the emblem of the god, its life-like representation in statues was intended to have an aphrodisiac effect on devotees since worship often took the form of an orgy.

The early Christian Church suppressed the cults and destroyed their phallic statuary with such zeal that very little of it remains. Even where the castrating Church Fathers were not responsible, there is something about an erect penis on a stone statue which invites vandalism and erosion.

Although most of the art was destroyed, the phallus has reared its head again from time to time to the consternation of the ecclesiastical authorities. A wooden statue of Priapus with a gigantic phallus known as 'Il Santo Membro' (The Holy Member) appeared incongruously together with more familiar figures in church parades in the Kingdom of Naples as late as the eighteenth century.

The regenerative capabilities of the phallus were also seen in Provence. Here the

LA MUSIQUE EN DELIRE.

unsuspecting St. Foutin de Varailles suffered further martyrdom at the hands of revivalists who credited him with all the attributes of Priapus. His shrine was regularly found to be decorated with wax phalluses brought as offering by the pious and the wine used in libations was sold as a powerful aphrodisiac.

It has been suggested that our own culture expresses its aggressive phallicism in the ever-taller buildings (known increasingly as 'cloud fondlers') which dominate the skyline of many cities in the West. They may be phallic symbols, but as Freud himself said: 'sometimes a cigar is just a cigar'.

PHILTRES AND POTIONS

The potentially consumable aphrodisiacs included in this book are either foods or recipes, or herbs which folk tradition has credited with the ability to stimulate desire. Things such as Spanish Fly, absinthe and mandrake are included only so that people who might be tempted to try them are reminded that they are deadly.

Almost as numerous in the abundant literature on aphrodisiacs are substances and recipes which are of little interest to anyone except medievalists or students of abnormal psychology. These 'philtres and potions' have been excluded for a variety of reasons. For example there is no good reason why screech owls should be troubled by people wanting their tail feathers when there are more palatable aphrodisiacs. Other substances have beem excluded because they are unlikely to appear in the inventory of even the most comprehensive health food stores e.g. crocodile semen; panther's breath.
(See also SEX MAGIC)

PHILTRUM

The groove in the centre of the upper lip below the base of the nose. In Tantra this is regarded as a highly erogenous area for women with a meridian connecting it to the clitoris.
(See also TANTRA)

PILLOWS AND CUSHIONS

Bedrooms intended for lovemaking as well as sleeping should be well-equipped with these useful items. In many of the more exotic lovemaking positions additional support is essential. In variations of the frontal positions a simple pillow under the woman which raise her middle can sometimes increase her pleasure enormously.

PILLOW BOOKS

A Japanese term for the sex manuals and aphrodisiac literature which were kept in the traditional lacquered wood pillow.
(See EROTIC LITERATURE; JAPAN)

PINE KERNELS

Known also as 'pine nuts', these feature in many Arab aphrodisiac concoctions – usually combined with honey.

PISTACHIO

A delicious, sweet nut probably originating in the Levant. Pistachio was mentioned in the Bible and was recorded in Persia as early as the fifth century BC. Because of its delicate flavour and green skin the pistachio is popular with confectioners. As an aphrodisiac it was especially popular in Arab countries.

POMANDERS

Decorated, scented oranges which seem to have been popular from the Late Middle Ages. Properly prepared, a pomander can be used to perfume underclothes and linen for up to ten years. Pomanders are also love charms: maidens would concentrate on their loved one during the lengthy process of inserting the cloves.

To make a pomander a thin-skinned orange should be studded with cloves. When the entire surface is covered, the orange is rolled in a mixture of orris powder, cinnamon, nutmeg and other blended spices which is firmly pushed in between the clove heads. The orange is then stored (in a brown paper bag) in a warm, dark, dry place for several weeks. When the orange is quite hard, the excess spice powders may be tapped out and the pomander decorated with ribbons.

POMEGRANITE

The juice and flesh of this exotic fruit are considered an aphrodisiac in most of the countries where they are grown. Part of the reason for this may be the pomegranite's association with fertility rituals: in China they were traditionally burst on the floor at wedding feasts; in ancient Greece they were eaten at Dionysian orgies.

Pomegranite juice is also available as grenadine syrup.

(See PLATE 10)

POMPOIR (See KABBAZAH)

POSITIONS

The use of different sexual positions to lend variety to lovemaking is an aphrodisiac technique common to all schools of erotology. Individual postures from India, China and Japan appear throughout this book. For the main groups of positions see ADAM AND EVE (Frontal); CROUPADE (Rear); CUISSADE (Rear straddled); and FLANQUETTE (Front straddled).

Although a variety of postures and sensations does have aphrodisiac value for most people, and sexual technique is undoubtedly important, attitude and sensitivity is more important. Sexual technique – however accomplished – is only a beginning.

POSTILLIONAGE

A technique of stimulating your partner's anus with a finger tip during lovemaking or just before orgasm.
(See also BOTTOMS AND BUTTOCKS; FEUILLE DE ROSE)

POWER

According to Henry Kissinger 'power is the ultimate aphrodisiac.' Unfortunately the drives involved in achieving great power (or wealth) prevent all but a few from enjoying such rewards since, like fetishes, those things tend to become an end in themselves.

PRAWNS

A valued aphrodisiac like most seafood: prawns appear more regularly in erotic cuisine than some other varieties, perhaps because they are a convenient size for mutual feeding.
(See also SEAFOOD)

PREGNANCY AND LACTATION

Women become more aware of their bodies during pregnancy – sometimes in a negative way but also positively. The sensitivity in a pregnant woman's nipples will often intensify with their increasing pigmentation, and her partner should be aware of this. Although more gentle sexual postures will become necessary (e.g. *spoon fashion)* pregnancy does not necessarily mean an end to sexual relations. Even if penetration is not desirable, the unique significance which sex takes on at this time for a woman lends a very special quality to all lovemaking techniques.

During lactation a women may be strongly aroused by an infant sucking at her breast. Nature made the process pleasurable for sound biological reasons and it is an important reminder – particularly to men – of the complexity of the human sexual response.

PRENKHA

The woman sits on her lover's lap with her foot braced against his shoulder. The slow rocking movement which is now possible is an orgasm-delaying technique.

Prenkha

QUINCE

Although inedible from the tree, the fruit of the quince can be made into delicious preserves and jellies. These have been regarded as an aphrodisiac for many centuries. In the language of flowers, quince blossom is the most unequivocal statement of love one lover can give to another: 'I will forsake all others and be faithful only unto you for the rest of my days'.

RADISH

The women of the harem 'were not suffered a radish or cucumber to their diet except it first be sliced'. The phallic shape of many radishes may explain their reputation as aphrodisiacs: or it may have more to do with their hot taste and the red colouring of some varieties. Radishes, which have been eaten by Man since pre-history, have a marked diuretic effect.

RATI'S WAY

A comfortable and adaptable position for protracted lovemaking. The woman sits on a chair or high cushions and her lover kneels between her legs. Both his hands are free to caress her.

RED

Much has been written about the colour red. Red is the colour of blood and fire, it is the colour of power and the universal colour of magic. It is also the colour of sex. Our skin reddens when we are excited; our lips, nipples and sex organs, which are red already, intensify in colour with erotic stimulation. With all these

Rati's Way

128

Reversed Position

Radish

Turnip

PLATE 12

complicated associations – The Scarlet Women; Red Light Districts – it is not surprising that a large number of supposedly aphrodisiac foods are red. The colour itself, which our brains are programmed to notice, is stimulating. The advertising industry uses red for the same reason, because we notice it. And of course it is the aphrodisiac colour: 'See that girl with the red dress on . . .'

REVERSED POSITION

In the Chinese tradition this posture is know as 'Overlapping Fish Scales.' Pace and penetration are entirely within the control of the woman: it is a visually exciting position for her partner.

REVERSE LOTUS

Both partners make love in the Lotus Position. Adepts of Hatha Yoga find the posture comfortable and use it in their lovemaking.

RHINO HORN

The quack who hit upon the idea that the hardened hair which forms the phallic 'horn' could be sold to the gullible as an aphrodisiac has much to answer for: a

Reverse Lotus

129

great deal of blood and a tragically endangered species.

RICE

A symbol of fertility: the practice of throwing it at weddings imitates the ejaculation of male semen. The wild forms are more commonly included in aphrodisiac recipes.

RISING

A relatively comfortable and satisfactory sexual position if only the woman raises her legs – she can hold her ankles to maintain the posture, or press her legs against her partner.

The Japanese 'rising position' (below) refers to the woman rising on her lover as she rides him.

ROCKET

The young shoots of rocket are eaten in salads or chopped and sprinkled over other dishes. The Romans credited the plant with strong aphrodisiac qualities – Martial called it 'lustful rocket' – and it was traditionally sown around the shrines of the phallic god Priapus.

(See also PHALLUS and PLATE 5)

No other flower has as many erotic associations as the rose: it is sacred to the love goddess in all the great mythological traditions. The colour of traditional roses, the evocative shape of the petals, and the intense perfume make it the archetypal female emblem. In the Persian myth all roses were white until the nightingale, unable to bear the pain of unrequited love for the rose, pressed a thorn deep into its heart.

Rosa centifolia. *Rosier à cent feuilles.*

The aphrodisiac power of the rose lies in its perfume (Rose Bulgar) and in magic. There is no more erotic gift for a woman than red roses. But never put red and white together: it is the symbol of separation, of the doomed love of Tristan and Isolde, of death.

(See PERFUME AND SCENT; RED; SEX MAGIC)

ROSE BULGAR

The finest and most precious of all the rose perfumes: Rose Maroc is heady, Turkish Rose is delicate, but Rose Bulgar unmistakably erotic. Cleopatra scented the sails of her famous barge with the essence of Damascene rose and it announced her arrival over the water long before she could be seen.

The roses from which Rose Bulgar is made grow in the foothills of the Balkans. They are picked in the early morning when all the essential oil is concentrated within the flower: each kilogram of oil is the precious yield of more than five tons of blossom.

Even if none of the other essential oils appeals to you and you would rather buy your perfume from one of the great perfume houses, do experiment with Rose Bulgar. One tiny and incredibly expensive phial will last a very long time and will transform your bath into something from the Arabian Nights.

(See also ESSENTIAL OILS; PERFUME AND SCENT)

ROSEMARY

An aromatic herb with sad associations – 'rosemary for remembrance' – and some more cheerful applications in the kitchen. The Romans valued it as an aphrodisiac, particularly in hot, spicy dishes.

(See also ESSENTIAL OILS)

RUSTIC

In this asana the man's legs are raised and his partner squats on her haunches. If he is properly supported on cushions, and she is sufficiently supple, this posture gives the woman an exceptional grip on her lover's penis.

SAFFRON

This very expensive spice was widely used as an aphrodisiac in the ancient world. The Greeks believed that its effect was even stronger in women and that a diet rich in saffron made a woman think of little but sex.

The English herbalists make constant reference to saffron's ability to make people 'merry' and cheerful. Whether directly or by improving their sex lives is not made clear.

An Arab aphrodisiac recipe consisted of saffron, orange blossom, dates, anise, carrot and egg yolk cooked with honey and a little water. The magnificent Spanish seafood dish paella may be more palatable for most people – but use real saffron and not turmeric which is often used and is a very poor substitute.

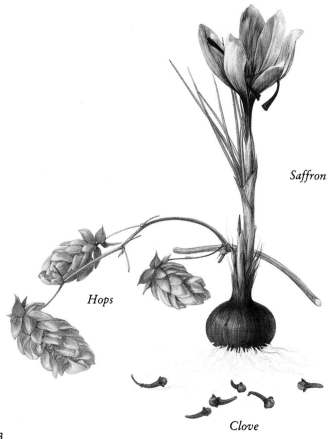

Saffron

Hops

Clove

PLATE 13

When the battle losses of the ancient Greeks had been particularly heavy, the women were encouraged to drink infusions of sage which was supposed to improve both their sexual appetite and their fertility. Hippocrates recommended the same method of increasing the population after the plagues which frequently afflicted cities.

Sage

Garlic

PLATE 14

ST. JOHN'S WORT
(*Hypericum perforatum*)

This perennial herb with its distinctive yellow flower has a long association with magic and witchcraft. Its reputation as a sexual stimulant may have less to do with the essential oils and hypericine which it contains than with the tradition that it must be picked naked at mighnight.

The freshly picked flowers of St. John's Wort, or the dried shoots, can be taken as an infusion (one teaspoon to a cup of water).
(See WILD PLANTS for methods and precautions)

SALIVA

Taoist texts, and to a lesser extent the Hindu and Arab erotic manuals, place considerable emphasis on the exchange of saliva between partners. The saliva of a sexually-excited woman was thought to retard the ageing process in a man (modern research confirms that regular sexual exercise certainly will).

Saliva exchange is practised by other mammals. Its function is not properly understood but it may well be the origin of kissing.

Saliva is also a natural and readily available sexual lubricant. Its advantage over creams and jellies is not only aesthetic, it is also the correct temperature and does not over-lubricate and reduce sensitivity.

(See also KISSING)

SALVIA
see SAGE

SAME SEX RELATIONSHIPS

Although this book is aimed principally at heterosexuals, many of the practices, games and recipes can equally be enjoyed by homosexuals.

Human beings are essentially bisexual and are capable of responding sexually both to their own and the opposite sex. Various factors determine whether a man or woman will be predominantly heterosexual or homosexual – whichever it is you should enjoy your sexuality. To retain some 'same-sex' response if you are heterosexual is perfectly normal. Guilt is not normal – and not necessary.

If you are concerned about these issues see the section at the beginning of the book on PROBLEMS.

SANDALWOOD

The warm, rich aroma of sandalwood is found exciting and 'male' by some women. The essential oil of sandalwood is manufactured in the Indian province of Mysore and is an important ingredient in many soaps and toiletries.

SATYRION (See IRIS)

The culinary uses of this perennial plant are a comparatively recent application – the Romans grew it specifically as an aphrodisiac. Satureia, as they called it, was sometimes added to food but more commonly sprinked on wine or taken with honey.

SEAFOOD

In all cultures at all times any encyclopedist, doctor, sexologist or quack writing about aphrodisiacs has included fish.

Why is seafood the universal aphrodisiac?

The answer is not hard to find after browsing through some of the aphrodisiac foods which people in different cultures have believed to be sexually stimulating. There are certain common features which emerge as the essential characteristics of aphrodisiac food. All seafood fulfills most of the requirements; with the addition of a spicy sauce some seafood fulfills all the requirements!

Seafood is nutritious and healthy, containing little fat but excellent protein as well as valuable minerals associated with sex: zinc; iodine, phosphorus and other traces.

Seafood is associated with a fertility deity and with the worship of that god. In this case the goddess of love herself, whether as Greek Aphrodite, Roman Venus or Norse Freya – all sea-born.

Seafood has a sensual texture. It feels much more interesting than meat in the mouth. Often there is additional tactile stimulation from holding seafood while we eat it. And of course the shapes are often strongly suggestive.

Seafood often comes in those colours which we find erotically interesting, notably white and red. Lobster, crab and other crustaceans are often both.

Seafood can be rare and exotic. Perhaps to justify the expenditure to ourselves we often credit exotic foods with aphrodisiac qualities. The best example is caviar, but lobster or abalone can also be expensive.

Seafood has an evocative smell. It often mimics our own sexual aroma.

Seafood even has elements in its taste which are salty and reminiscent of human sexual fluids.

The only element missing from seafood is the hot, peppery, diuretic element which is common to many supposed aphrodisiacs. This must make prawns with a horseradish dip (sea cucumbers are too limp) the ultimate stimulant for women and oysters with tabasco the best for men. Mussels in a provencale sauce would be a good compromise, or lobster with capers.

(See also ANCHOVY; BOUILLABAISSE; CAVIAR; LOBSTER; MUSSELS; OYSTERS, PRAWNS)

SEA HOLLY (See ERYNGO)

SEMEN

The aroma of semen – whether from one of more than thirty different elements it contains or by association – has an aphrodisiac effect on many people. There is no

それでも　わろくおぢさん　それさう　さうき　より　どふも　ぼうらい

るそへゐんの　ぶりーしいとうあるあ　いろをみんちょ大きくそねるここ　てるをりそきーグめてまょ　まるらーう下ぬころびちサアく　わうこーくられね

きんさ　わろく　るやら　ねれて　ろや　ろう　サア

harm in swallowing semen providing there is no questions of AIDS: it contains
useful trace elements and sugars and represents about thirty-five calories. It is
literally a matter of taste.

(See also FELLATIO)

Not only does our sense of smell take up a surprisingly large proportion of our brain, its situation is unusually privileged. There is immediate access of information: human beings react to smell even more quickly than to pain. The complex of which 'smell' is a part is also concerned with emotion and the memory function, sexuality and controlling hormone production.

Although we are not usually aware of it, but only of its effects, we have a very sophisticated olfactory communication system with direct access to those parts of the brain where we can be said to 'live'.

In some cultures more importance is placed on the sense of smell than in others. Among the southern Slavs a mother will ask her son if his lover smells good to him, in the way that mothers in other cultures may ask if she is pretty. The importance of scent in sexual attraction and compatibility is extremely important even if some human cultures find it 'impolite' or disturbingly animal.

The unseen, unsuspected messengers who carry all the coded information about sex between us are pheromones. We live our lives in a ceaseless sexual crossfire of pheromones, unaware of what messages we are receiving or are ourselves transmitting.

Perfume may imitate some pheromones and help to disperse others, but it cannot replace substances which are Nature's own aphrodisiacs. Pheromones may have a greater impact on our lives than we yet understand. Unknown to us they operate the biological machinery of attraction and repulsion, with a hot line straight to our endocrine system and the seat of our emotions,
(See also CASSOLETTE; PERFUME AND SCENT)

SEX MAGIC

This entry is not concerned with ritual magic where sex is merely a component or the nastier aspects of medieval mumbo-jumbo, but with some of the simple folk spells which have been used as aphrodisiacs.

Throughout Europe village 'wisewomen' would, for a suitable fee, bake spiced cakes which were used as aphrodisiacs. These were prepared as near as possible to the naked body of the woman who commissioned them so that she could feel the heat from the fire which was baking the cakes. The same heat would subsequently be transferred to the loins of the man who ate the cake. Presumably this ritual enabled the old women to see if there was any physical reason for the spouse's lack of passion which could be treated with folk medicine. The slow baking process was also an opportunity to pass on some useful sexual tips.

Apples, and one or two other fruits, were used in love magic which involved sleeping with the fruit near to the skin or in 'privvy places' and then persuading the object of your desires to eat it. This sounds like early experimentation with pheromones (see CASSOLETTE; SENSE OF SMELL).

Charms and amulets to bring sexual 'luck' or prowess were very common and usually phallic. The world's museums abound with examples from different cultures, often to the embarrassment of the more repressed keepers who keep them away

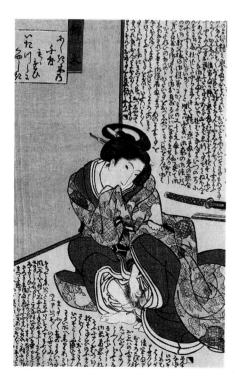

from the public. What is involved here of course is imitative magic and the belief that an object has merit which can be transferred. The amulet need not have come from a magician – art itself (and some of these phallic charms are beautifully made) is magical. Perhaps the greatest erotic art, such as shunga with its exaggerated penises, is in part a sophisticated version of the same idea.

(See also EROTIC ART; JAPAN; PHALLUS)

SEX TOYS

Different cultures have produced a wide variety of sex toys but they are all permutations on the same themes. The most common, dildos, are dealt with separately. Less common, presumably because they are less satisfactory, are merkins or artificial vaginas. ('Merkin' was also used to describe the charming pubic wigs of different colours worn by fashionable ladies in the eighteenth century, also called bowsers).

Penis rings, whether made from ivory or rubber, are designed to help and maintain erection. They may additionally have raised parts intended to stimulate the clitoris. The hard rings were made to measure by oriental craftsmen – experimentation can damage the hydraulics. Soft rings, which work in the same way by stopping the return blood supply, may be successful but why experiment on your own when there is good counselling advice available (see PROBLEMS at the beginning

of the book) and there may be a much simpler solution?

Penis extentions, much favoured by the Japanese, are a waste of time and can be dangerous for the woman because they are hard. Every book about sexual technique says it, but perhaps it should be said again: size does not matter. If Nature gave you a big penis be grateful, at a distance you will look stunning. You will still need to learn the techniques of lovemaking which are far more important for giving pleasure to your partner.

Vaginal balls are an interesting masturbation device for women. They are called rinno-tama; Burmese bells; Chinese bells; Thai beads; Ben-Wa and other variants. Unfortunately the best quality rinno-tama are hard to find and the cheap plastic ones may not be successful. The idea is to walk or rock with the one, two or three linked hollow balls inside you. They are weighted to move erratically. Geishas and oiran spent many hours waiting for their clients in traditional Japanese society where rinno-tama were invented. Some wrote exquisite poems, some played with rinno-tama. Some did both:

> *'The device of the two copper plums*
> *With silver in them*
> *Slowly and very slowly*
> *Satisfies.*
> *Just as all finishes*
> *Dew falls on my clenched hand'.*

> *'I would rather the bean flowered yellow*
> *And he were here . . .'*

SHOUTING MONKEY

The famous Chinese lovemaking position where the man lies on his back and his partner rides him with her legs drawn up. See the Hindu equivalent, *Black Bee* for a full description.

SKIN

The whole surface of your body and your lover's body is there to be enjoyed. Some parts are more sensitive than others but in compensation they may look and feel more sensual to the toucher. The pleasure is both in touching and in being touched. If you make love only with the parts of you which protrude from pyjamas or are accessible under nightdresses you are not using the largest sex organ you possess – your skin.

If you live in a cold climate try to organize the bedroom so that it is warm because lovemaking should be conducted in the nude. If you both like frou-frou nightwear, start by wearing it and have him undress you slowly during foreplay. But always make love naked, or you are missing out on a great deal of secondary stimulation and pleasure.

(See MASSAGE; PATTES D'ARRAIGNEE; TONGUE BATH; TOUCH)

Sky-Foot

The couple in the painting are using a Yoga breath-control technique as part of their lovemaking. Tantric practices like this are only for adepts, but the purpose of many of them is male orgasm delay.

Snails

The edible snails which live in vineyards have been considered an aphrodisiac delicacy since Roman times. A sauce containing parsley and garlic – both reputedly aphrodisiacs in their own right – can only serve to heighten the effect.

The snail is a common metaphor for the clitoris in the Orient, perhaps because it tends to peep out in a similar way and then disappears again.

Shampoo

A term which appears in Sir Richard Burton's translation of Kama Sutra and elsewhere. Shampooing simply means massaging the whole body as you do the hair to wash it. The delightful though mysterious practice which always seemed to end in lovemaking in ancient India still can!

(See Massage)

All the erotic traditions feature variants of this lovemaking position which is as old as mankind. Some of the most surprising and charming depictions are to be found carved high up in Gothic cathedrals by craftsmen who must have relied on myopia – either real or feigned – on the part of the authorities.

SPANISH FLY

Better described as Blister Fly this irritant poison causes ulceration of the entire alimentary canal and even perforation of the stomach. By the time the lower end of the urinaray tract is inflamed to a point where it may cause a painful erection your kidneys will have been destroyed. (See PROBLEMS in the Introduction).

SPINACH

This excellent vegetable which can be cooked or picked young and eaten in salads (which preserves its nutrients) contains vitamins A, B, C, E and K and many useful minerals. Spinach was brought into Europe by the Moors and probably originated in Persia. A wonderful Turkish hors d'oeuvres is chopped cooked spinach in thick yoghurt with garlic – *ispanah*.

Although its iron cannot in fact be assimilated, spinach is nevertheless extremely nutritious and generations of children were not misled by Popeye. As spinach has long been regarded as an aphrodisiac it is interesting to reflect on what the further adventures of Popeye and Olive Oyl may have been.

SPLIT BAMBOO

A famous lovemaking position where the woman sits on the man's lap, her back supported by pillows. See 'Cobra Hood' for the demanding Yogic equivalent.

Split Bamboo

143

Spontaneity

An important and much-neglected aphrodisiac. If you are all dressed up and ready to go out and the mood takes your partner to make love – get undressed. Or if you really cannot be late improvise something hasty. Forget 'later', the moment will have passed. Be pleased that someone desires you: few appointments are as important as preserving that.

If you are more prone to having such whims than your partner, do not suppress them. Explain how important it is, persist. The same applies if you are in the open air , or travelling. Something can usually be organized. Life is much too short to miss opportunities – even if you have to replace all your buttons with velcro!

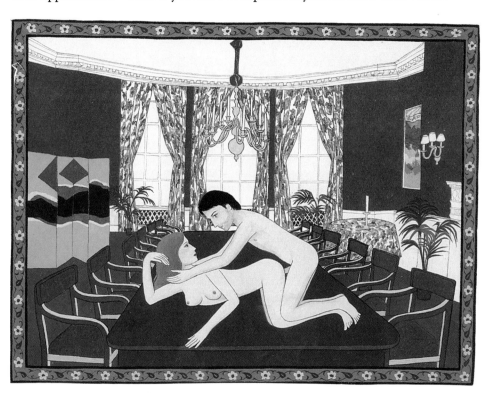

Spoon Fashion

A lovemaking position where the couple fit together like spoons lying down, the man entering the woman from the rear. See *Mandarin Ducks* for a full description.

Stallion

Known in Chinese sex manuals of the Ming Dynasty as 'Jumping Wild Horse'. A tiring posture for the man if it is sustained for too long.

Striptease

The professional version is dealt with under Dance and Performing Arts – this is your performance. Removing your clothes for your doctor and removing them for your lover should be two completely different operations (unless of course they are one and the same person).

Stallion

A race to get out of your clothes and into bed because you want each other so badly is the only excuse (and a good one) for not making a piece of theatre out of undressing. How can you expect your partner to desire your body if you unload it from your clothes like groceries from a shopping bag?

The performance does not have to be the Dance of the Seven Veils to music (although it can be sometimes). Slowing down helps. Show him your breasts, show him your pubis: each new revelation should be preceded by a little tension, however brief, before it is made.

A word for the audience: watching in either vest or socks is prohibited – a naked man in socks is a very effective anaphrodisiac for a woman, and vests are not much better. Audience participation is welcome, take over the undressing if you like. Interludes are also welcomed: kiss her nipples when they are revealed, before resuming your seat on the bed.

Finally, and also for the man: Your clothes should not be removed slowly (unless you are playing striptease games too). Partially clothed men are not very exciting – naked ones are. Nor should you painstakingly arrange everything in the wardrobe like a valet. Pay attention to your lover not the crease in your trousers

Good lovers make appreciative audiences. And appreciation is a wonderful aphrodisiac for a woman.

SUCKING A MANGO

An oral technique described in Kama Sutra. It involves noisy, wet sucking as the name implies: the penis is treated like a luscious tropical fruit. Oral lovemaking became more popular in later Hindu love manuals.

SUSPENDED POSITION

This position gives wonderful perineal stimulation for the woman but should only be attempted in water unless your lover is a circus strong man. One slip in standing positions where the woman's weight can suddenly bear on the penis can permanently damage its hydraulics.

SWASTIKA

This asana takes its name from the ancient Hindu sun symbol which has come to have terrible associations in the twentieth century. It is a striding position in which she controls most of the movement and in doing so assumes the familiar shape.

SWINGS

If you and your lover have access to a gymnasium when no-one else is there, or are as wealthy as the Orissan prince in the painting and can have your own, there

Swastika

146

are all sorts of aphrodisiac games to be played. His equipment looks as if it could stand the shock, but the penis can be damaged when erect so take care.

More generally available and private are garden seats. These were a favourite venue for the Chinese and offer a variety of pleasant sensations for relaxed al fresco lovemaking.

TANTRA

An Indian cult which its adherents maintain is older than Hinduism: this would make it a religion of the Indus Valley civilization of 2000 BC. Its followers see Yoga as being essentially Tantric, but although Yoga is now considered one of the six orthodox systems of Hinduism. Tantra has suffered constant persecution and suppression. For the purposes of this book which is concerned only with collecting some ideas about sexuality from different cultures (including the West's own folk tradition), Tantra and Yoga must be regarded as very similar. There is the same emphasis on breath control and asanas, but Tantra has more to say about sex than Yoga. That is not because Tantra is only to do with sex. The philosphy of Tantra covers every aspect of human life and embodies many highly-sophisticated concepts. There are many different sects and sub-sects, but it is a misconception that Tantra is concerned principally with sex – but this book is.

Perhaps the most important sexual point Tantra has to make is that lovemaking can be protracted. For a Westerner not interested in mysticism this does not mean that sex must always be a marathon, but given the difference in sexual response between men and women it is good if it sometimes can be. Many of those sexual positions identified as showing Tantric influence are specifically designed to maintain sexual tension while delaying (male) orgasm.

The other Tantric sexual truth which comes naturally out of the first is that the whole body can, and should, be used in lovemaking. This is the opposite of the orgasm-targetted, penis-centred approach of most Western males. In Tantra, the sexual unit is the couple, the importance of the woman paramount .
(See also BANDHA; INDIA; YOGA)

TARRAGON

This powerful herb has a wide range of culinary applications and has been used in some traditional aphrodisiac recipes.
(See BRIDE CAKES AND WEDDING FOOD)

THYME

One of the herbs most commonly used for 'strewing' by the ancients to provide a scented floor covering which releases its aroma as it is bruised by the feet. A

combination of thyme and roses was considered especially aphrodisiac and was used to prepare Roman houses for orgies.
(See also HONEY)

─────────────────────── *TIGER'S TREAD* ───────────────────────

In the Arab tradition this sexual position is called *Camel's Hump*. The woman bends from the waist in a standing position and her partner enters her from the rear.

─────────────────────── TOMATO ───────────────────────

Once called 'love apples', or 'Peruvian Apples' which indicates their South American origins, tomatoes were still regarded as a mainly ornamental plant in eighteenth-century France. Unfortunately the unique musky scent and taste which were the origins of their aphrodisiac reputation is largely absent from many tomatoes now available in the shops.

The herb basil has a particular affinity with tomato. The chopped fresh herb sprinkled over sliced tomato with olive oil and lemon juice (or vinegar) makes a superb salad.
(See also BASIL)

─────────────────────── TONGUE BATH ───────────────────────

This is licking your lover's body as an arousal technique. The idea is to stimulate the skin, slowly building the tension towards oral games and lovemaking. In Japan this technique is called *the Tree*. Some lovers like to anoint one another with honey, yoghurt or some other suitable substance. It is interesting that the word 'lechery' is derived from licking.

─────────────────────── *TORTOISE* ───────────────────────

The woman sits on her lover's thigh. Both partners have their knees drawn up and a hand free for fondling.

Transcendent

TOUCH

'Angoisse du toucher', an aversion to being touched which is rare in its pathological form but otherwise widespread in Northern Europe and America. This denial of our biological inheritance is sad because – as some generous eccentrics understand – touch can be reassuring, comforting or simply friendly as well as sexual.

The hysterical aversion to being touched is usually explained by sufferers as a quite natural dislike of being touched in a sexual manner by ill-intentioned people. The point is of course that they are probably not being touched sexually in their own lives and therefore cannot take a balanced view of well-intentioned bear hugs or occasional pats.

Years of social conditioning are not easily overcome but the place to begin is in bed. Touching another's body and having them touch yours is the most wonderful part of sex: simply being together naked is extremely pleasurable. If touch is given its proper place in the bedroom then it will automatically take its rightful place elsewhere.

TRANSCENDENT

Although many Tantric lovemaking positions have applications to those not interested in the ritual others, like this bandha, do not.

TRIDENT

The woman assumes a widely-yawning position and her lover 'strides' into her. Good for clitoral stimulation if he rides high. In all yawning and deep penetration positions the man must never lunge awkwardly: bruising an ovary is as painful as hitting a testicle.

TRIPOD

One of the less hazardous standing positions: if your balance is not good use a wall for support. The Chinese name for this is the mysterious *Bamboo at a Shrine*. The *Tripod* is sometimes a useful position for spontaneous al fresco sex.

TRUFFLE

Entire books have been written on the aphrodisiac value of this pungent fungus which is found in white, black and red forms. Truffles grow underground which makes the gathering (usually with dogs) difficult and the price high. It is not possible to cultivate truffles commercially.

The Romans enjoyed truffles, as did George IV who instructed his ambassadors to establish a regular supply to the royal kitchens. Truffles were recommended to Napoleon as a means of increasing his potency.

Many patés contain truffles which is so strongly flavoured that only a minute amount is needed. Finest of all is the black truffle which is particularly good with game and is an essential ingredient in much aphrodisiac cooking.
(See EROTIC CUISINE)

Trident

TURNAROUND

In this technique the woman mounts her lover and after a few strokes swings one leg over his chest until she is facing the other way. The same pattern is then repeated.

(left) Tripod   (right) Turnaround

Utpiditaka

— UTPIDITAKA —

A sexual technique meaning 'high squeeze'. In this position the man supports the woman but is, essentially, passive. She is the active partner, milking his penis with her vagina by using the holding technique.
(see KABBAZAH)

— VALERIAN —
(*Valeriana officinalis*)

A perennial herb with a very long history of use as an aphrodisiac. Among the Celtic peoples women wore a sprig of valerian between their breasts to attract lovers. In the Middle Ages valerian was known as cetwale and was added to beer; later it became known as 'drunken sailor' and was used by tavern prostitutes.

The roots should be collected after the leaves have died back, washed and dried in the shade. One teaspoon per cup of water can be taken as an infusion, but not more than the equivalent of one cup a day and not for long periods.
(See WILD PLANTS for methods and precautions)

— VANILLA —

Its name happens to be the diminutive of vagina, but vanilla owes its reputation as an aphrodisiac to Madame Pompadour. The stimulants with which she excited Louis XV were mostly delicious: vanilla was added to whipped cream or chocolate.
(See also EROTIC CUISINE)

(Verbena officinalis)

Its name means 'sacred herb' in Latin which since it also has a reputation as a sexual stimulant may indicate a connection with an ancient fertility cult.

Vervain is available as a herb tea, especially in Germany. To make your own infusion dry the flowering plant in the sun and add two teaspoons per cup of water. (See WILD PLANTS for methods and precautions)

──────────── *VICTORY* ────────────

The painting from Jaipur shows a transitional stage. Having penetrated his lover the man is moving forward until he is straddling her with his penis bent away from him under tension 'to polish the jewel of her clitoris'.

──────────── *VIENNA OYSTER* ────────────

Sexual gymnastics and training were the vogue in fin de siecle Vienna. This position is only of interest to gymnasts: the woman lies on her back, crossing her feet behind her head. Her lover then penetrates her by lying on top of her.

──────────── *VINE* ────────────

This striding position, Lataveshta, demands considerable suppleness in the man. If he is long and rides high this position give good clitoral stimulation.

──────────── VOICE ────────────

'One accent from thy lips the blood more warmes,
Than all their philtres, exorcism and charmes'.

These lines from Robert Burton's Anatomy of Melancholy, refer to the erotic excitement which the human voice can create. While higher tones are thrilling, both men and women find deeper voices more aphrodisiac.

Of course the voice of a loved one is thrilling even if he or she speaks like Mickey Mouse. Nature does not bless everyone with a deep voice or indeed prodigious sexual equipment. In both cases how you use them is the important thing.

Vine

WATER

Fire may be the most passionate of the elements, but water is the most erotic. Everything about water is sexual: the sound it makes, the way it moves, the way it caresses every part of the skin surface when we swim. The goddess of love came from the sea: Aphrodite means 'born of the surf'.

Water is also a very useful way of overcoming gravity, and buoyancy can enable lovers to achieve most of the Hindu standing postures which on dry land are difficult and even hazardous. Even if you have access to a private swimming pool the sea is better – for buoyancy, aesthetically, because salt is preferable to chlorine.

WHEEL

The naive perspective of the painting rather confuses a simple asana where the woman rides the man, constantly turning on him to vary the visual and physical sensation for both of them. Unless you are agile, rising and falling on your lover's penis while turning is easier if there is something overhead to grasp.

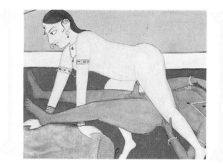

Wheel

WHEELBARROW

This popular position gives good perineal stimulation for the woman but it is better as an intermediate stage in lovemaking rather than a final posture for orgasm unless she is already very excited.

WIFE OF INDRA

A famous lovemaking posture from Kama Sutra. The woman is in the yawning position fully supported by pillows and cushions. Her partner kneels or squats before her, riding higher and pressing down on her as they approach orgasm.

Wife of Indra

WILD PLANTS

It is strongly recommended that you OBTAIN ALL HERBS FROM A QUALIFIED AND REPUTABLE HERBALIST. If you want to collect them yourself remember that this book is not intended as an identification guide although some wild plants are illustrated. Each plant is given both its popular and botanical name to enable you to find it in botanical reference books. There are several excellent guides to edible and medicinal plants which you must consult before attempting to gather any of the plants mentioned in this book. Even then you would be well-advised to go collecting with an expert as many plants look similar to untrained eyes. Remember, many of the most deadly poisons known to man are present in large quantities in some plants.

The details of how to dry and store plants and are also important. Where you pick plants is significant too since many fields have been sprayed with pesticides. The laws protecting plants are another factor and with some plants one part is edible and another is poisonous. A GOOD PLANT IDENTIFICATION GUIDE IS ESSENTIAL, preferably with an expert companion: there are always local botanists and societies who are pleased to help – even if it is only to identify plants after you have collected.

PREPARATION AND DOSAGE

Because plant identification guides may not give the dose and preparation method this has been indicated, together with the part of the plant to be used. The method of preparation in most cases is infusion. Place the recommended quantity of the plant in the bottom of a standard-sized teacup (not metallic). The chopped or shredded material should be measured in teaspoons – not heaped. Fill the cup with boiling water and cover with a saucer. Leave this to stand for the time indicated where this is important. Drink as soon as possible thereafter. Maceration is used where plants have delicately balanced ingredients and are steeped in cold water. The time differs and is given with each plant.

Unless otherwise indicated the maximum daily intake of the prepared herbal 'tea' is one cup per day.

———————————— WINE ————————————

BACCHUS ET ARIANE.

One of the world's great sensual pleasures. There are wines to suit every taste, every mood, every occasion – and every pocket. Wine should delight the eye, the nose and the taste before it goes on to delight the rest of you. Treat it as part of the

Wrestler

ritual of lovemaking, hone your senses with it, enjoy it together – but not too much. The old saying is 'one cup for health; two cups for love; and three for sleep'. You can of course choose your 'cup' which need not be the exiguous restaurant object. But try not to cheat like the Emperor Charlemagne who boasted that he seldom had more than one cup of wine in an evening but failed to mention that a Frankish cup resembled a bird bath.

The white wines best suited to lovemaking – before and after only, unless you are making a day of it – are those with intense perfume and good fruit rather than the flinty-dry types. For the rich there are the great German wines, but Sancerre is also wonderful as are many of the fragrant wines made from the Chardonnay grape in Australia and California.

Red wine is a little more difficult in an erotic context but more rewarding if you get it right. Fine clarets demand (and deserve) too much attention but could be enjoyed during a long pre-lovemaking meal if table and bed rate of similar importance for both of you. Burgundy is probably better or intensely-flavoured Italians like Venegazzu. The spectacular red wines of Australia may be best of all for lovers.

Dessert wine offers many possibilities from Beaume de Venise with its female muscat scent and taste, to the rich wonders of port and madeira.
(See also ALCOHOL; CHAMPAGNE; EROTIC CUISINE)

WOODRUFF
(*Asperula odorata*)
This perennial herb is one of those which European herbalists believed to be 'provocative to venery'. The fresh or dried herb (preferably picked just before flowering) can be taken as an infusion. Two teaspoons of the chopped herb per cup of water, allowed to stand for ten minutes.
(See WILD PLANTS methods and precautions)

WRESTLER
This position is a sexual variant of a Yoga asana and should not be attempted by the untrained.

X POSTURE
When lovers lean back fully, with the penis inserted in a frontal position, they form the *X posture*. This position is good for leisurely lovemaking and can be maintained for quite long periods.

Yawning

A typical example of a group of sexual postures which all involve the woman's legs being opened as widely as possible, her knees drawn up. All yawning positions involve deep penetration and require controlled thrusting from the man.

If the man moves in and out with an undulating rhythm it is the technique the Chinese call *reeling off silk*.

Ylang-Ylang

An intensely sweet and flowery essential oil derived from the Ylang-Ylang tree which grows in Madagascar. It has a good reputation as a stimulating aroma for men from the time when it was in vogue as a simple floral perfume.
(See also ESSENTIAL OILS; PERFUME AND SCENT)

Yoga

One of the six systems of orthodox Hindu philosophy. There are many different Yogas but that most familiar outside India is Hatha Yoga, the Yoga of physical power. This is an arduous and lengthy voyage of self-discovery in eight stages, each involving greater mental and physical control. In the more advanced stages sex is seen as a hindrance rather than a help in the search for enlightenment, which is one of the main differences between Yoga and Tantra which in many other respects are similar.
(See also TANTRA)

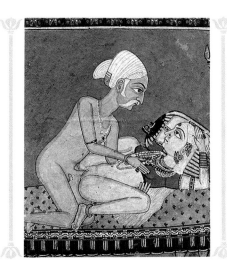

Yawning

Zulu Style

Various cultures have adopted different methods of controlling adolescent sexuality. The least healthy is surrounding sex with a wall of guilt and shame. The Victorian

educators added a sadistic twist by propagating the rumour that even sex with yourself was not only a reason for feeling guilty but also caused everything from blindness to insanity.

Another method was 'clothed intercourse'. This has been surreptitiously practised by Western teenagers who would have been surprised to learn that their counterparts in Turkey and among the Xhosa were encouraged to do it. Not very satisfactory, certainly not an effective contraceptive, but more enlightened than guilt and repression.

Zulu elders in traditional Zulu society had a better method. The young men and women were permitted to make love, at certain times, by moving the boy's penis between the girl's thighs. Lovemaking to all intents and purposes, with good clitoral stimulation for her and a reduced risk of unwanted pregnancy. The Latin term is coitus inter femora which some people indulge in for pleasure rather than from necessity. The Zulus called it 'the Wiping of the Spears'. Whatever else it is, it is not a particularly good birth control method – the great Zulu king Chaka is said to have been conceived during the Wiping of the Spears.